THE SEARCH FOR THE
ELEMENTS

THE
SEARCH
FOR THE
ELEMENTS

Isaac Asimov

BASIC BOOKS, INC.

Publishers   *New York*

5 4/6

65-194

Fourth Printing

© *1962 by Basic Books Publishing Co., Inc.*
Library of Congress Catalog Card Number: 62–15833
MANUFACTURED IN THE UNITED STATES OF AMERICA
Designed by Tere LoPrete

*To Ruth and Leon Svirsky
and October in Westchester*

10/65

CONTENTS

THE SEARCH FOR THE ELEMENTS

1

THE GREEKS WONDER

Twenty-six centuries ago, in the year 640 B.C., one of the most remarkable men in all history was born. His name was Thales, and he was born in the city of Miletus on the western coast of Asia Minor, then a part of Greece.

Thales had the kind of mind that busied itself with everything—with brilliant results. As a statesman, he persuaded the various Greek cities of Ionia to unite for self-protection against the non-Greek kingdoms in the interior of Asia Minor. As a scientist, he made important discoveries in mathematics and astronomy. In fact, Thales can be considered the founder of mathematical reasoning. He worked out a system of deriving new mathematical truths from those already known. This method, called deduction (from a Latin word meaning "to bring out"), is the basis of modern mathematics, so Thales can be looked upon as the first true mathematician.

Thales learned astronomy from the Babylonians, whose studies of the heavens had enabled them to make a calendar of the seasons and explain eclipses of the sun.

To ancient peoples the sudden darkening of the earth

by an eclipse was very frightening. They supposed that some monster was swallowing the sun. People would run from their houses to the village square, beating pots and crying wildly to scare off the monster. Since the sun always reappeared in a few minutes, the pot-beaters were sure that their efforts had saved it.

The Babylonian astronomers were the first to discover that the moon, passing in front of the sun, was responsible for eclipses. After they had figured out the motions of the moon and the sun, the astronomers astounded people by actually predicting when an eclipse would come.

Thales, returning to his country from Babylon, introduced the new astronomy to the Greeks. In 586 B.C. he predicted that a total eclipse of the sun would occur in Ionia the following year. As it happened, the eclipse came on a day when the armies of two nearby peoples, the Medes and the Lydians, were about to engage in battle. Both armies were so frightened by the darkening of the sun that they immediately signed a treaty of peace.

Thales became known throughout Greece as a scholar. When Greek writers drew up lists of their "seven wise men," all of them put Thales of Miletus at the top of the list.

He was the first Greek "philosopher" (meaning "lover of wisdom"). There were those who sneered at his philosophical bent, saying in effect, "If you are so wise, why aren't you rich?" Thales, the story goes, silenced these scoffers with a shrewd piece of business. Deciding from his studies of the weather that the coming year would be a good one for the olive crop, he bought up all the olive presses (used to squeeze the oil out of the olives) and then charged high prices for their use. This coup made him a wealthy man. Then he quit business. As a philosopher, he loved wisdom more than money.

He was also the original "absent-minded professor."

One night, as he walked along the road studying the stars, he fell into a ditch. A servant girl who helped him out laughed: "Here is a man who wants to study the universe and yet cannot see what is going on at his own feet."

It was certainly true that Thales wanted to study the universe. Indeed, of all his contributions to science, perhaps the most remarkable was his posing of a simple but profound question: What is the universe made of? Men have been pursuing Thales' question for thousands of years since he first asked it.

The story of the search for the answer to the question is one of the great detective stories of science. That is the story with which this book concerns itself.

THE GREEKS' ELEMENTS

Thales wanted to know: What is the stuff that makes up the sun, the moon, the stars, the earth, rocks, sea, air, and the living things on earth? It was the most natural thing in the world to suppose (as even modern scientists have supposed) that if you could break down all these things to their ultimate nature, you would find they were all made of one simple substance—that is, one elementary building block.

The word "element" comes from the Latin *elementum.* Nobody knows the origin of the Latin word. One suggestion is that the Romans may have said that something was "as easy as L-M-N," just as we say "easy as A-B-C." At any rate, *elementum* came to mean something simple from which complex things were built.

Thales, after long thought, decided that the element out of which all the universe was built was water. In the first place, there was a great deal of water on the earth—whole oceans of it. In the second place, when water evaporated it apparently became air. Air also seemed to turn back to water in the form of rain. Finally, rain falling on the ground might eventually harden, he thought, and thus be-become soil and rock.

Other Greeks took up Thales' interesting speculation, and came to different conclusions. His own pupil, Anaximander, thought that water could not possibly be the building block of the universe, because its properties were too specific. The materials everyone knew were varied and had many contradictory properties. Some were wet and others dry; some were cold and others hot. No known substance could combine these opposite qualities. Therefore the basic element of the universe must be some mysterious substance unlike anything with which man was familiar.

Anaximander of course could not describe this substance, but he gave it a name—"apeiron." He maintained that the universe had been put together from a limitless supply of apeiron. Some day, if and when the universe was destroyed, everything would turn into apeiron again.

Most of the Greek philosophers couldn't go along with this idea. To say that the universe was composed of something which existed only in imagination was no answer, they felt.

Anaximenes, a younger philosopher of Miletus, nominated air, instead of water, as the element of the universe. Since everything was surrounded by air, he reasoned that the earth and the oceans were formed by the congealing or condensation of air.

Heraclitus, a philosopher of Ephesus, near Miletus, had another idea. He insisted that the ultimate element was fire. The most important and universal feature of the universe, he said, was change. Day followed night and night day. One season gave way to another. The face of the earth was continually altered by rivers and earthquakes.

Trees, and structures, rose and fell into decay. Even man was ephemeral—he was born, grew up, and finally died. All this changeability was epitomized best of all by fire. This "substance," continually changing its form, blazing up and dying down, represented the essence of the universe, in Heraclitus' opinion. So he concluded that the universe must be made of fire in various manifestations.

This kind of argument might have gone on for quite a while, with one substance after another being championed as *the* element of the universe, if somebody had not come along with an idea so beautiful that it silenced the embattled advocates. The idea came from the school of the famous Pythagoras.

Pythagoras, a Greek philosopher who migrated about 530 B.C. to the city of Crotone in southern Italy, founded a mystical school of philosophy based on the study of numbers. The school made important discoveries about irrational numbers (such as the square root of two), the nature of sound, and the structure of the universe. Pythagoras himself may have been the first man to suggest that the earth was round and not flat. He is also, of course, reputed to be the author of the Pythagorean theorem on the right triangle, but it is not certain that he was the first to propose it.

Our hero, however, is not Pythagoras but a bright young member of his school named Empedocles. Pondering the problem of what the universe was made of, he came up with a proposal that neatly combined the views of the champions of single elements. Why insist that everything was made from just one element? Couldn't there be several elements? As a matter of fact, this idea made more sense. It would explain the different properties of matter that were observed. Thinking about these properties, Empedocles decided that there must be four elements: earth, water, air, and fire, representing, respectively, solidity, liquidity, vaporousness, and changeability. Most objects, he said, were combinations of these four elements.

Take a log of wood. Since it is solid in its usual form, it may consist mainly of the solid element, earth. When it is heated, it burns, so it contains the "element" fire also. On burning, it gives off vapor—a form of air. Some of the vapor turns to drops of water; the wood, then, must contain water as well. In short, wood is made of all four elements—earth, fire, air, and water. So reasoned Empedocles.

His idea of the four elements caught on at once and became popular among the Greek philosophers. It was later developed further by Aristotle (384-322 B.C.), the greatest philosopher of ancient Greece.

Aristotle was an all-round scholar—a one-man encyclopedia. He contributed original ideas to every branch of science in his time. On Empedocles' notion concerning the four elements, Aristotle built a general theory about the nature of all matter in the universe.

He suggested, among other things, that each element had its own natural place in the scheme of things. Earth, he believed, belonged at the center of our universe; around this core was the water of the oceans; a layer of air, in turn, surrounded the earth and oceans; and beyond that, high in the atmosphere, was the natural realm of fire (which often showed itself in the form of lightning). Each element sought its own level. Thus, a rock in the air would fall to earth, its natural level; fire always rose toward the high region of fire; and so forth.

The stars in the heavens, Aristotle decided, must belong to a completely different category. Unlike the changeable matter on the earth, they seemed unchanging and eternal. Furthermore, the objects in the heavens moved in a fixed sphere, neither rising nor falling. Therefore they must be made of an element completely different from any on earth. So Aristotle invented a fifth element which he thought of as composing all of the universe outside the earth. He called it "aether"; later philosophers named it "quintessence," Latin for "fifth substance." Since the fifth element was supposed to be perfect (unlike the elements of the imperfect and changing earth), we still use "quintessence" in English to mean the purest form of anything.

Aristotle conceived another notion which influenced men's views of matter for thousands of years. He noted that coldness and warmth, wetness and dryness seemed to be fundamental properties of the elements. But properties could be changed: something cold could be warmed, something wet could be dried. Presumably, then, by altering the properties in some way, you could change one element into another. This notion, as we shall see, was the gleam in the eye that led to chemistry, but it started men off on the wrong foot, with ludicrous results.

2

ALCHEMY AND ELIXIRS

Soon after Aristotle's time, Greek culture suddenly spread far and wide over Asia and Africa, thanks to the military adventures and conquests of Alexander the Great. He brought the Greek language and Greek knowledge to Persia, Babylonia, and Egypt. In return, the Greeks picked up a great deal of knowledge from the Babylonians and the Egyptians.

Alexander founded many new cities in the lands he conquered. The largest and most important was Alexandria (named after himself, of course). He started this settlement, at the mouth of the westernmost branch of the Nile, in 332 B.C.

Alexandria became the capital of a new Egyptian kingdom ruled by the descendants of Ptolemy, one of Alexander's generals. It was a melting-pot of ancient cultures: a third of its population was Greek, a third Jewish, and a third Egyptian.

Ptolemy I established a "Museum" in Alexandria. Here, in what might be called a university today, he gathered all the philosophers he could, offering them support and security. His son, Ptolemy II, carried on, collecting books for the Museum until it had the largest library in the ancient world. As scholars flocked to the Museum to take advantage of its library and other facilities, Athens declined as the center of Greek learning and Alexandria took its place. It remained the intellectual center of the ancient world for 700 years.

The scholars of Alexandria continued in the tradition of the Ionian philosophers and of Aristotle. But under Egyptian influence, their thinking about the makeup of the universe and the nature of the elements took a new direction. Most of the Greek thinkers had merely reasoned about the physical world, without doing much observing or experimental testing of their ideas. In the view of the dominant Greek philosophy, as expressed by Plato, the ideal was more important than the material; therefore the important truths about the essential nature of things would be discovered by pure thought rather than by messing around with material things. The Egyptians, on the other hand, were a completely practical people. They treated certain rocks—heating them with charcoal, for instance—to get metal out of them. They made glass from sand, and bricks from clay. They prepared dyes and medicines and many other substances.

The Greeks gave the name "chemia" to this art of treating materials so as to change their nature. They may have got the word from "Chem," the Egyptians' name for their own land. "Chem" was also the Egyptian word for black. Some people think that "chemia" therefore was intended to mean "black magic." As far as the Egyptians were concerned, they called their land "black" for a very good reason which had nothing to do with mystery or magic. It was a reference to the black, fertile soil of their Nile homeland, which contrasted with the yellow sands of the desert.

When the Arabs later conquered Egypt, they prefixed "chemia" with "al," the Arabic word for "the," so the word became "al chemia," and eventually in English "alchemy."

The early craftsmen who worked with metals, dyes, and other substances kept their techniques secret, in order to keep a monopoly on their products and charge high prices (a practice not unknown today). This added to the mystery surrounding alchemy. It also made gobbledygook out of most of the alchemical writings. In fact, alchemy was at first almost a religion, and the Egyptians considered the god Thoth the god of alchemy. The Greeks assigned this honor to their god Hermes, who was their counterpart of Thoth. They therefore called alchemy the "hermetic art." We still use the word to this day; when something is sealed air-tight (a procedure the ancient Egyptians sometimes used in alchemy), we say it is "hermetically sealed."

THE GREEK ALCHEMISTS

The first Greek writer on alchemy whom we know of was a second-century worker with metal named Bolos Democritus. He tried to combine the practical knowledge of the Egyptians with the theories of Aristotle. Bolos Democritus knew that certain treatments could change the color of metals. For example, mixing copper (a red metal) with zinc (a gray one) would produce a yellowish alloy (brass). Its color was like that of gold. Bolos Democritus reasoned that it was but a step from forming the color of gold to forming gold itself. Since, according to Aristotle, both lead and gold were made up of the four universal elements (earth, water, air, and fire), couldn't lead be changed to gold merely by changing the proportions of the elements? Bolos Democritus began to experiment with all sorts of recipes for turning lead into gold.

This was the beginning of a long effort of more than

a thousand years to bring about "transmutation" of substances (from a Greek word meaning "to change completely"). The idea was taken up enthusiastically by so many people that as early as 300 A.D. an alchemist named Zosimus wrote an encyclopedia of alchemy which ran to 28 volumes.

Almost all the alchemical theories are considered nowadays to have been nonsense. But they were taken so seriously at the time that the Roman emperor Diocletian ordered all the books on alchemy to be destroyed, on the ground that if people learned how to make gold it would ruin the money system and destroy the economy of the Empire. His destruction of the books is one reason we know so little today about Greek alchemy. Perhaps if more of the books had survived, we would find some gems of real wisdom embedded in the nonsense. For instance, Zosimus described certain experiments in which he seemed to be talking about a compound which today we call "lead acetate."

In the fifth century Alexandria collapsed as a center of learning. After the Emperor Constantine made Christianity the official religion of the Roman Empire, Alexandria was attacked by the new converts as a center of "pagan" learning. Christian riots destroyed much of the great library and forced many of the scholars to flee. Thereafter Constantinople, the city Constantine had established as his capital, replaced Alexandria as the repository of Greek learning.

For nearly a thousand years, however, the Christian scholars devoted themselves to theology and moral philosophy rather than natural philosophy. The only important alchemist during those centuries in Constantinople was Callinicus. He invented "Greek fire," a mixture of substances for which the exact formula has been lost. It probably contained pitch and quicklime. Quicklime gets very hot when water is added, hot enough to set fire to the pitch. Greek fire could therefore burn fiercely in the sea. The armies of Constantinople used it to drive off invading fleets.

ISLAM AND ELIXIRS

In the century after Constantinople became the capital, the Roman Empire was overrun by uncivilized tribes from the north. By the year 500 the western half of the Empire was completely under the barbarians' control. And in the seventh century much of the eastern half, including Syria and Egypt, fell to the new religion, Islam, founded by Mohammed. The Arabian armies swept over Syria and Persia, then flooded across North Africa. They captured Alexandria in 640 A.D.

Culturally, however, the Arabs were conquered by the Greek tradition of learning. The Mohammedans, more hospitable to pagan knowledge than the Christians were, preserved the Greek natural philosophy in such Arabic centers of learning as Baghdad, Cairo, and Cordova.

Baghdad, the capital of the largest of the Mohammedan empires, reached the height of its power and glory in the eighth and ninth centuries. Today it is the capital of Iraq. Cairo, founded by the Moslems in the tenth century, became a great center in the thirteenth century. It is now the capital of Egypt and the largest city in Africa. Cordova, the capital of the Moslem kingdom established in Spain in the eighth century, declined in importance after its capture by the Spanish Christians in the thirteenth century, but it is still an important provincial city in the south of Spain.

The first Arabian alchemist of whom we have any record is Khalid ibn Yazid, who lived from 660 to 704. He was the son of one of the early Arabian caliphs and might have succeeded to the throne but for palace intrigues. Fortunately, he was more interested in alchemy than in politics; he retired thankfully from public life and devoted himself to his studies. He is supposed to have learned about alchemy from an Alexandrian Greek and to have written many books on the subject.

The important originator of Arabian alchemy, however, was Jabir. Jabir's lifetime coincided with the height of Baghdad's glory in the eighth century. He was the official alchemist at the court of Caliph Harun-al-Raschid and a personal friend of the Caliph's vizier Jafar—both of whom appear in many of the tales of the *Thousand and One Nights*. After the vizier fell out of favor and was executed, Jabir decided it was safest to leave the court, so he returned to Al-Kufa, a town about 90 miles south of Baghdad, where he had been born.

Many books and treatises are attributed to Jabir—so many, in fact, that some of them may actually have been written by other alchemists who put his name on them to get more attention for their books. This was quite a common practice in ancient times.

It appears that Jabir was a very careful alchemist. He wrote out the formulas for producing a number of new materials. Furthermore, he was not satisfied with the notion that all substances were made of Aristotle's four elements. He therefore pursued certain other ideas (which may have occurred earlier to the Greek alchemists).

Jabir considered the fact that metals and non-metals were altogether different in properties. Could both be composed of the same solid element, earth? He decided that metals must contain some special principle which, when added to earth in different proportions, produced the various individual metals. This principle, it seemed to Jabir, must exist in largest amount in mercury, because that metal was a liquid and therefore must contain little of the solid earth.

Jabir noticed further that certain non-metals would burn, whereas metals did not. Again he reasoned that there must be some special principle which, when added to a substance, gave it the property of being able to burn. He decided that sulfur must contain this principle in greatest quantity, because sulfur burned easily. His principle of inflammability was therefore "sulfur."

Jabir came to the conclusion that all solid substances were combinations of "mercury" and "sulfur" (that is, the principles which these represented). Therefore, if one could only alter the combination in lead, say, one might convert it to gold.

In the ninth century Baghdad produced a second great alchemist, properly known as Al-Razi, a name later changed by Europeans to Rhazes. He was probably of Persian descent, for his name means "the man from Rai" (an ancient town whose ruins are near Teheran).

At about the age of 30, Al-Razi visited Baghdad. There, the story goes, he was fascinated by the stories he heard from an apothecary about medicine and disease. Al-Razi decided to study medicine, and he ended as chief physician of Baghdad's largest hospital.

Al-Razi described his experiments so carefully that modern scholars can repeat them. He described plaster of Paris, for instance, and the manner in which it could be used to form casts holding broken bones in place. He also studied the substance we now call antimony.

Another Persian-born physician, perhaps the greatest medical man of the Middle Ages, was known as Ibn-Sina. After his books were translated into Latin, he became famous among European scholars under a mispronounced version of his name, Avicenna. He was born near Bukhara, a city northwest of modern Iran and now part of the U.S.S.R.

He wrote more than a hundred books on medicine (some of them very long) and listed hundreds of drugs and their uses. Naturally he became an alchemist, for many drugs were made by alchemical procedures. He was an unusual alchemist, however, in that he did not think transmutation was possible.

In this he was far ahead of his time. The alchemists were pursuing the transmutation of metals with increasing eagerness. Everyone wanted to discover the secret of easy riches. They hunted tirelessly for some mysterious substance, some dry and magical powder, which would bring about the change in "mercury" and "sulfur" that would form gold. The Arabs called the magic substance "al-iksir," from a Greek word meaning "dry" (which probably means that the Greeks started the search first). The word has come down to us as "elixir."

The alchemists naturally imagined that the wonderful elixir which would change cheap metals to gold would also have many other marvelous qualities. It would cure sickness, for instance, and make it possible for men to live forever. Even today we sometimes speak of medicines as "elixirs," and, in literary fancy, of an "elixir of life" which might make men immortal.

In later centuries the Europeans, thinking of the elixir as a hard, solid material, named it the "philosopher's stone."

After Avicenna, Arabic books on alchemy became nothing but mumbo-jumbo. The Moslem power and culture began to decline, too, as the empire broke up. But fortunately, Europe was beginning to emerge from its intellectual childhood and to take up the torch of science.

3

THE DECLINE OF MAGIC

During Europe's lowest period, between 500 and 1000 (sometimes called the "Dark Ages"), the western Europeans thought of the Moslems only as a devilish people with a false religion.

In 1096 the knights of western Europe launched the Crusades to win back the Holy Land, which had been under Moslem control for about 450 years. They captured Jerusalem and held it for 80 years, but after two centuries of continuous warfare the Christians were driven completely out of the Middle East. Most of it has been Moslem ever since, except for the new Jewish state of Israel and the partly Christian state of Lebanon.

The Crusaders found that the Moslems were more civilized and knowledgeable than they had supposed. They brought back news of new products used by the Arabs (such as silk and sugar) and of advances in medicine and alchemy beyond anything known in Europe.

Adventuresome European scholars began to seek out Moslem knowledge in places such as Spain and Sicily, where the Moslems had long been in control. They learned Arabic, and with the help of Moslem and Jewish scholars began to translate Arabian books into Latin.

The greatest of these early translators was an Italian, Gerard of Cremona (1114-1187). He travelled to Toledo, a Spanish city that had recently been captured from the Moslems. Working with Moslem scholars, he translated some of the alchemical books of Jabir and Al-Razi and the medical books of Ibn-Sina. He also translated some of the works of Aristotle and the great Greek mathematicians Euclid and Ptolemy.

As it happened, the revival of interest in Aristotle in western Europe was also stimulated by two great living interpreters of the Greek philosopher—a Moslem scholar, Averroes, living in Spain, and a Jewish scholar, Maimonides, in Egypt.

The newly discovered Arabian learning and the rescued Greek writing swept Europe. By the thirteenth century western Europe had begun to take the lead as the chief center of learning, and it remained the leader right down to the twentieth century.

THE EUROPEAN ALCHEMISTS

Naturally the European scholars took an immediate interest in Arabian alchemy. The first to do original investigation in this field was a German nobleman, Albert, Count of Bollstädt (1206-1280), usually known as Albertus Magnus ("Albert the Great"). He was also called the "Universal Doctor," because he studied Aristotle's books and seemed to his students to know everything.

Albertus Magnus proposed some recipes for producing gold and silver. But much more important (though nobody realized it at the time) was his description of a method for preparing arsenic, a grayish substance with some metallic properties. Minerals containing arsenic had been known to the Greeks and Romans and had been used by them as coloring matter. Pure arsenic, however, was a new thing. Albertus Magnus was the first to call the substance to the attention of European scholars, and he is traditionally given credit for its discovery.

Albertus Magnus had two particularly famous pupils —Thomas Aquinas (1225-1274) of Italy and Roger Bacon (1214-1292) of England. Bacon became an active alchemist. He popularized Jabir's notion concerning the principles of "mercury" and "sulfur." Some have credited Bacon with inventing gunpowder, but it now seems that the first European to make gunpowder was a German alchemist named Berthold Schwarz.

Another early European alchemist was Arnold of Villanova, Spain. Like many other alchemists, he made an important discovery while chasing the will-o'-the-wisp transmutation. He learned that certain vapors from burning charcoal were poisonous; what he had discovered (although he did not know it) was carbon monoxide.

Also in Spain, around 1300, was an alchemist who wrote under the pseudonym of "Geber," apparently to pass himself off as the famous Jabir. He would have been better advised to give his real name, for he was a true discoverer whose actual name is now lost. He was the first to describe the strong mineral acids, such as sulfuric acid and nitric acid.

These acids gave the alchemists new tools for treating materials. They could dissolve substances which had not been soluble in the weak acids (such as vinegar) known to the ancients. Geber's discovery is actually more valuable today than gold. Sulfuric and nitric acids have become the bases of industries such as fertilizers, explosives, dyes, and many others. If all the gold in the world were to disappear, it would hardly affect us, but loss of the strong acids would be a catastrophe.

At the time, only the search for a magic formula for making gold attracted mankind. Many were those who claimed success. One of the most famous was a Spanish scholar named Ramon Lully. He was supposed to have manufactured gold for King Edward I of England. Of course he had done no such thing; in fact, Lully seems to have been one of the few alchemists who didn't believe transmutation possible. Just the same, people were eager to believe the tale about his alleged achievement.

Fakers flourished. Quantities of "gold" coins (actually made of brass or gilded lead) were palmed off on the pretense they had been manufactured alchemically. There was so much counterfeiting of this sort that in 1313 Pope John XXII banned the practice of alchemy altogether, on the intelligent basis that transmutation was impossible and the alchemists were deceiving the people and hurting the economy.

In England, King Henry IV and later English kings occasionally granted some individuals permission to work on the gold-making problem, with the idea of controlling the gold themselves.

For two centuries after Geber, no real work of importance was done in alchemy. It was almost all fraud and mumbo-jumbo. Some of the practitioners got away with their "confidence game"; a few were exposed and punished severely—sometimes even hanged. The very word "alchemist" came to mean "faker."

There were some honest alchemists, of course. One was Bernard Trevisan of Italy (1406-1490). He spent his long life and fortune looking in vain for the secret of gold.

By the sixteenth century a new spirit began to animate natural philosophy, and it inevitably affected the alchemists. Notable among the new generation of alchemists was an eccentric Swiss named Theophrastus Bombastus von Hohenheim (1493-1541). His father taught him medicine and he himself studied minerals in Austrian mines. He wandered all over Europe, picking up knowledge wherever he went. Von Hohenheim turned his alchemical studies to finding a philosopher's stone to create medicines for treatment of disease, rather than to make gold.

One of the most famous Roman writers on medicine had been Aulus Cornelius Celsus. Von Hohenheim, rejecting the ancient Roman and Greek notions about disease, called himself "Paracelsus" (beyond Celsus).

In 1526, as professor of medicine in Basel, Switzerland, Paracelsus shocked the scholars of the time by publicly burning the books on medicine written by Greeks and Arabs. It took drastic actions such as this to shake science out of its slumber. The medical men were furious, but Paracelsus made them begin to question traditional ideas and think along new lines. He managed to cure some patients they were not able to help. His fame grew. He was not without a streak of fakery; for instance, he claimed to have discovered the secret of eternal life—but of course did not live to prove his theory. He died at the age of 50, apparently of a fractured skull suffered in an accidental fall.

Paracelsus added a third principle to "mercury" and "sulfur," which supposedly carried properties of metal and inflammability. What about non-metals that did not burn, such as salt? He decided that a third principle must represent this property, and he took "salt" as its embodiment.

Paracelsus was the first to describe zinc. Minerals containing this metal had long been used to make brass (a mixture of copper and zinc), but the metal itself had not been known, so Paracelsus is commonly credited with being the discoverer of zinc.

To this day the name of Paracelsus is almost synonymous with alchemy. But actually he is not the most famous alchemist. That distinction belongs to a man who, oddly enough, contributed very little to alchemy or to science. He was simply a man who in his time (the time of Paracelsus also) achieved a popular reputation as a magician. Legend said he made a pact with the devil. The name of this alchemist, immortalized by Goethe, was Johann Faust.

At the end of the sixteenth century, alchemy began to make the transition to a true science. In 1597 a German alchemist named Andreas Libau, usually known by the Latin version of his name, Libavius, paved the way by compiling all the knowledge the alchemists had collected. His book, *Alchemia,* can be considered the first good textbook on the subject. Libavius made an important contribution of his own: he was the first to describe methods for preparing hydrochloric acid.

Let us, then, sum up the answers that men had pro-

Table 1

THE ELEMENTS OF ANCIENT AND MEDIEVAL TIMES

ELEMENT	DATE PROPOSED	PROPOSED BY
"Water"	c. 600 B.C.	Thales
"Air"	c. 550 B.C.	Anaximenes
"Fire"	c. 550 B.C.	Heraclitus
"Earth"	c. 450 B.C.	Empedocles
"Aether"	c. 350 B.C.	Aristotle
"Mercury"	c. 750 A.D.	Jabir
"Sulfur"	c. 750 A.D.	Jabir
"Salt"	c. 1530 A.D.	Paracelsus

posed, up to this time, to Thales' question: What is the universe made of? They are listed in Table 1.

What a result from 2,000 years of thought! Men's notions of the nature of matter were still very crude. No one had isolated a single element or found any rational way of combining elements into compounds.

But a revolution was in the making. The seventeenth century came in like thunder, shattering old ideas and clearing the air for a fresh start in science.

4

A NEW START

The revolution had begun in 1543, two years after Paracelsus' death. In that year the Polish astronomer Nicholas Copernicus published his startling theory that the sun, not the earth, was the center of the universe. It took more than half a century for the scholars of the time to reconcile themselves to this profound change in point of view. In the end, the overthrow of the old ideas in astronomy also brought about a new attitude toward science generally.

Francis Bacon (1561-1626) was one of the first to give formal expression to the new way of thinking. In 1605 he published a book called *Advancement of Learning*. This treatise cleared away the mysticism that beclouded science. Then in 1620 he presented a new method of reasoning in a book called *Novum Organum* (the title was taken from Aristotle's *Organon,* a treatise on deductive reasoning).

Bacon pointed out that deduction, the method of reasoning from assumed truths, was insufficient for learning the nature of the physical universe. It was successful in mathematics, but "natural philosophy" (science) called for a different approach. One must study nature itself—observe, collect facts, put them in order, and work out theories or laws based on the facts.

Bacon did not himself apply his "inductive" method to investigation of the physical world. It was his great contemporary, Galileo Galilei (1564-1642), who put the method into practice.

THE SCIENTIFIC REVOLUTION

Galileo is perhaps the first person, of those I have mentioned so far in this book, who can be called a true scientist. While he was still a young man, he began to act strangely (for those times). For instance, when he was 17, he noticed one day that a swinging chandelier in the Cathedral of Pisa seemed to take the same time to complete a swing whether it made a wide swing or a short one. Galileo promptly went home and did some experiments. He set up pendulums of various kinds and timed their swings with his pulse beat. Sure enough, his conjecture proved to be correct: a pendulum on a string of a given length always oscillated at the same rate, regardless of its weight or the width of its swing.

At the time, to most philosophers this sort of behavior looked silly. Measuring, testing, playing with strings and balls—that was not the way of a real thinker. But as Galileo continued his experiments, investigating one phenomenon after another by the most accurate methods he could devise, he impressed his contemporaries more and more. By rolling balls on inclined surfaces, he disproved Aristotle's notion that objects of different weights would fall at different speeds. Galileo went on to build a telescope and make observations which completely upset the time-honored Greek picture of the heavens. He saw stars that were invisible to the naked eye; he saw mountains on the moon and spots on the sun; he saw that the planet Jupiter had four small moons.

Galileo was not the first man in history to observe, measure, and experiment. But he was the first to elevate this method to a system and popularize it. He wrote books and articles about his findings (in Italian rather than in Latin) which were so interesting and clear that the scholars of Europe began to be won over to the new system. For that reason most people feel that what we call "science" really started with Galileo. (Actually, the word "science" didn't come into use until well into the nineteenth century; up to that time scientists called themselves "natural philosophers." Even today, students who do advanced work in science earn the degree of Ph.D.—"Doctor of Philosophy.")

The scientific revolution that Galileo initiated affected all the sciences, including alchemy.

In 1604 a German named Thölde published a book titled *The Triumphal Chariot of Antimony,* which announced the discovery of two new substances—antimony and bismuth.

Antimony had actually been known for thousands of years, though not as an element. Minerals containing antimony had been used in Biblical times as "eye shadow"; Jezebel is supposed to have applied it when she "painted" her face." The Greek alchemists may even have known how to prepare pure antimony, and archaeologists have found an ancient Babylonian vase made of antimony.

Thölde said that the book he published was originally written by a fifteenth-century monk named Basilius Valentinus. But it was so advanced that there is some doubt it was written so early, and even doubt that there ever was such a person as Valentinus. Thölde himself may have been the author.

The new scientific approach to studying matter was

exemplified by Jan Baptista van Helmont (1577-1644), a Flemish alchemist born near Brussels. He was particularly interested in vapors. He studied the vapors formed by burning charcoal and the bubbles of vapor in fermenting fruit juice. Since vapors were a shapeless form of matter in a state that the Greeks called "chaos," van Helmont adopted this name for vapor, but he spelled it according to the Flemish pronunciation—"gas."

The only gas known up to that time was air. But van Helmont found that the gas produced by burning charcoal had properties which were not the same as ordinary air. For instance, a candle would not burn in this gas. He called it "air sylvestre" ("air from wood"). We know it today as carbon dioxide.

Then there was a German alchemist named Johann Rudolf Glauber who also made careful observations. His most famous discovery was "Glauber's salt," which we now know as sodium sulfate. Glauber had a bit of the Paracelsus about him. He decided that his new salt was a cure for almost everything, and he called it *sal mirabile* ("wondrous salt").

DOWN WITH THE OLD ELEMENTS

The first man to ask Thales' old question in the new spirit of science was an Englishman named Robert Boyle.

Boyle (1627-1691) was born in the town of Lismore in southern Ireland. He was the fourteenth child of the Earl of Cork. He visited Italy in 1641, just a year before Galileo died. There he came to know the great man's work, and he returned to England with a profound interest in Galilean science.

Like van Helmont, he became especially interested in the behavior of gases, and he made many experiments. His best known studies are those he did with air in a closed vessel under various amounts of pressure. He found that the volume of air was reduced in direct proportion to the increase in pressure on it. This simple but important discovery is the now famous "Boyle's law."

In 1645 Boyle, together with a group of friends who were interested in the new science, formed a club called the "Philosophical College." The club soon went into eclipse, because of the popular rebellion against the Crown and the beheading of King Charles I. Boyle and his friends were aristocrats and thought it wise to keep out of sight for a while. But after the British people restored Charles II to the throne in 1660, the club came into the open again. It was now under the protection of the king, so it was renamed the "Royal Society." The Society has served as a forum for European science ever since.

In 1661 Boyle wrote about his discoveries and theories in a book called *The Sceptical Chymist*. Boyle called himself a "chymist" (from the original Greek word *chemia*), because "alchemist" had fallen into such ill repute. Thereafter alchemy became "chemistry" (by a slight change in Boyle's spelling).

Boyle described himself as a "sceptical" chemist because he questioned the old Greek notions of the elements. He felt that a completely new start had to be made in the search for the elements.

One had to begin by defining clearly what an element was. The elements should be defined as the basic substances from which all matter was made. This meant that an element could not be broken down into any simpler substances. Therefore one way to find out whether a suspected element was really an element was to try to break it down. Another method of investigation was to combine substances into compounds and then separate them into the elements again. In short, the best way to identify the elements was by experimenting.

How did the old "elements" stand up according to this new outlook? Start with "fire" and "earth." Fire was not a substance at all, only the glow of heated matter. As for earth, it could be shown that earth was made up of many simpler substances. So neither was an element, by Boyle's definition.

Water and air were knottier problems. At the time Boyle's book was written, these two substances could not be broken down to anything simpler, so they might be elements. But in 1671 Boyle did an experiment which eventually turned out to be proof that they were not elements, though he did not know it at the time. He treated iron with acid and produced some bubbles of gas. He thought that the gas was just ordinary air. But other chemists later found that this gas from iron burned, and even exploded. And more than a hundred years after that, it was discovered that, on burning, the gas combined with part of the air to form water. That showed that water was a compound, not an element. Furthermore, other experiments eventually showed that water could be broken down into two gases which would recombine to form water. And the fact that the explosive gas combined with only a part of the air also proved that air was a mixture of substances.

So none of the four ancient Greek "elements" was really an element after all.

UP WITH THE NEW

On the other hand, some of the substances that the Greeks knew but didn't call elements eventually did turn out to be elements. One of them was gold. The alchemists had been trying the impossible; all their hard work could not form gold from other substances because it was itself simply an element. Only the modern alchemy of nuclear physics has succeeded in changing one element into another.

Along with gold, the ancients knew six other metals which in the end proved to be true elements: silver, copper, iron, tin, lead, and mercury. In addition, they knew two non-metals which were later identified as elements—sulfur and carbon.

To summarize, in Table 2 I am listing the nine substances known to the ancients that are now considered to be elements by Boyle's definition. We have no definite information as to exactly when or by whom they were discovered.

Table 2

THE CHEMICAL ELEMENTS KNOWN TO THE ANCIENTS		
CHEMICAL ELEMENT	YEAR DISCOVERED	DISCOVERER
Gold	?	?
Silver	?	?
Copper	?	?
Iron	?	?
Tin	?	?
Lead	?	?
Mercury	?	?
Carbon	?	?
Sulfur	?	?

What about the "elements" of the alchemists? Well, Jabir coined the names of two—"mercury" and "sulfur." But the mercury and sulfur "principles" that he conceived (and out of which he thought he could make gold and glass by mixing them in proper proportions) were not the actual elements. The properties of the chemical elements mercury and sulfur are altogether different from the alchemical principles of Jabir's "mercury" and "sulfur." As for "salt," Paracelsus' principle, every schoolboy knows today that it is a compound of sodium and chlorine.

Still, in their search for a way to make gold the alchemists did discover several real elements. I listed these in Table 3, along with the names of their supposed discoverers and the approximate dates.

Table 3

ELEMENTS DISCOVERED BY THE ALCHEMISTS

CHEMICAL ELEMENT	YEAR DISCOVERED	DISCOVERER
Arsenic	c. 1250?	Albertus Magnus?
Antimony	c. 1450?	Basilius Valentinus?
Bismuth	c. 1450?	Basilius Valentinus?
Zinc	c. 1530?	Paracelsus?

Altogether, then, by Boyle's time 13 substances which eventually turned out to be elements had been discovered.

5

THE AGE OF
PHLOGISTON

Although the 13 substances listed in the last chapter are now known to be elements, this does not mean they were necessarily considered elements in Boyle's time. The chemist of 1661 could not really be sure that gold, for instance, could not be split into simpler substances.

Boyle himself didn't think that gold was an element. Perhaps another metal, such as lead, might be split into substances which could then be recombined to form gold. In other words, lead and gold might be compounds of still simpler elements. Boyle even persuaded Charles II to repeal Henry IV's old law forbidding the manufacture of gold, because he believed that the law stood in the way of scientific advance.

For a hundred years and more after Boyle, the attempt to make gold by transmutation continued unabated. Partly this was because the royalty of the time remained extremely interested in such projects. Government had become much more expensive than in the Middle Ages, but the system of taxation remained medieval. Although the poor peasants were ground down by the tax rate, collection was so inefficient and governments so corrupt that the kings of the seventeenth and eighteenth centuries were always short of money. They were constantly tempted to believe any alchemist who swore that gold could be made from iron. Thus Christian IV, King of Denmark from 1588 to 1648, coined money out of "gold" prepared for him by an alchemist. So did Ferdinand III, the Holy Roman Emperor from 1637 to 1657.

Sometimes the fakers went just a bit too far. One was caught and hanged by a German margrave in 1686. Another alchemist was hanged in 1709 by the Prussian king, Frederick I. Both the margrave and the king had been taken in through their hunger for gold.

Perhaps the most famous alchemical faker of all time was a Sicilian named Guiseppe Balsamo (1743-1795). In his youth he worked as assistant to an apothecary and picked up a smattering of chemistry and medicine. He also had a glib tongue, a talent for forgery, and no morals at all. He cooked up fakeries of every sort, claiming, for instance, that he had lived for thousands of years, that he could make gold, and that he had secret elixirs which would confer great beauty and long life.

Under the name of Count Allesandro di Cagliostro, he operated with remarkable success in the France of Louis XVI. He founded secret societies, manufactured fake gold, defrauded foolish people in every walk of life. Finally he made the mistake of getting involved in the theft of an expensive necklace from a jeweler under the pretense that it was for Queen Marie Antoinette. This landed him in a French jail in 1785.

The "affair of the Queen's necklace" was very bad publicity for Marie Antoinette, who was supposed by many to have been involved in the crooked dealings (although she wasn't). It helped to bring on the French Revolution in 1789. Cagliostro had managed to get out of jail by then. But his luck had run out. He was jailed in Rome for secret-society shenanigans and this time he got a life sentence.

Cagliostro is an important character in several of the historical romances of Alexander Dumas, who, unfortunately, treats him quite sympathetically.

Even legitimate scientists continued to pursue the search for gold. The most startling case is that of Isaac Newton (1642-1727), probably the greatest scientist who ever lived. Newton spent a great deal of time in an alchemical quest for the secret of making gold—with no more success than lesser minds had had.

The lingering belief in alchemy gave birth to some other curious but popular ideas. One was a new theory about combustion. About 1700 a German physician named George Ernst Stahl, taking his cue from the Jabirian idea of the burning "principle" (sulfur), gave a new name to this principle—"phlogiston," from a Greek word for "inflammable." According to Stahl, when a substance burned the phlogiston left it and escaped into the air. The ash that was left behind could burn no more because it was completely free of phlogiston.

Stahl conceived another idea which was shrewder than he knew. He said the rusting of metals was a process just like the burning of wood. (This is true: in both cases the process of oxidation.) Stahl theorized that when a metal was heated, phlogiston escaped from it, leaving a "calx" (which we would call rust).

His theory seemed to explain the facts of combustion so neatly that it was accepted by most chemists. Almost the only serious objection to it was that the calx of a rusting metal was heavier than the original metal. How could the metal lose something (phlogiston) and end up heavier?

But most eighteenth century chemists didn't worry about this. Some suggested that perhaps phlogiston had "negative weight," so that a substance lost weight when phlogiston was added to it and gained weight when phlogiston left it.

NEW METALS

In spite of all the hanky-panky, the "age of phlogiston" produced some pretty important discoveries. An alchemist of the time actually discovered a new element—the first (and last) alchemist who definitely identified an element and told exactly when and how he had found it.

This man was a German named Hennig Brand. He is sometimes called the "last of the alchemists," but actually there were many alchemists after him. Brand, seeking the philosopher's stone to make gold, somehow got the strange idea that he might find it in human urine. He collected some urine and let it stand for two weeks. Then he heated it to boil away the water and reduce it to the solid residue. He mixed this bit of solid with sand, heated the combination strongly, and collected the vapor that came off. When the vapor cooled, it formed a waxy, white solid. And lo and behold! this substance glowed in the dark!

What Brand had isolated was phosphorus, named from a Greek word meaning "light-bearer." It glows because it combines spontaneously with air in a very slow combustion. Brand did not understand its properties, of course, but the isolation of the element (in 1669) was a spectacular discovery and made a sensation. Others rushed to prepare the glowing substance. Boyle himself prepared some phosphorous without knowing of Brand's prior work.

The next element was not discovered until nearly 70 years later.

Copper miners in Germany occasionally came across a certain blue mineral which did not yield copper, as the blue copper ores usually did. The miners found that this particular mineral sometimes made them sick (it contained arsenic, chemists learned later). The miners therefore called it "cobalt," after the name of a mischievous earth-spirit in German legends. Glass-makers found a use for the mineral: it gave glass a beautiful blue color, and a fairly large industry grew up on this blue glass.

In the 1730's a Swedish physician named George Brandt became interested in the chemistry of the mineral. He heated it with charcoal, the standard way of extracting a metal from a mineral, and he finally reduced it to a metal which behaved like iron. It was attracted by a magnet— the first substance other than iron that had ever been found to possess this property. It was definitely not iron, for it did not form a reddish-brown rust, as iron did. Brandt decided that it must be a new metal, like no other then known. He called it cobalt, and it has been known by that name ever since.

So Brand had discovered phosphorus and Brandt had found cobalt (the similarity of names of the first two element-discoverers is quite a coincidence). Unlike Brand, Brandt was no alchemist. In fact, he helped to kill alchemy by dissolving gold in strong acids and then recovering the gold from the solution. This explained some of the tricks alchemical fakers had used.

It was a pupil of Brandt who made the next discovery. Axel Fredrik Cronstedt became a chemist and also the first modern mineralogist, for he was the first to classify minerals according to the elements they contained. In 1751 Cronstedt looked into a green mineral which miners called *kupfernickel* ("devil's copper"). He heated the calx of this mineral together with charcoal, and he, too, got a metal that was attracted by a magnet, like iron and cobalt. But whereas iron formed brown compounds and cobalt formed blue ones, this metal gave rise to compounds which were green. Cronstedt decided it was a new metal and named it nickel, short for *kupfernickel*.

There was some argument as to whether nickel and cobalt were actually elements or merely compounds of iron and arsenic. But the point was settled in 1780 by still another Swedish chemist, Torbern Olof Bergman. He prepared nickel in purer form than Cronstedt had, and he presented good arguments to show that nickel and cobalt contained no arsenic and were indeed new elements.

Bergman was a powerful force in the new chemistry, and several of his students went on to discover new elements.

One of these was Johan Gottlieb Gahn, who worked as a miner in his youth and remained interested in minerals all his life. Chemists had been working on a mineral called "manganese," which turned glass violet. ("Manganese" was a misspelling of "magnesia," another mineral with which some medieval alchemist had confused it.) The chemists were sure that the violet mineral must contain a new metal, but they were not able to separate it by heating the mineral with charcoal. Gahn finally turned the trick by powdering the mineral with charcoal and heating it with oil. Naturally the metal was named manganese.

Another Bergman pupil, Peter Jacob Hjelm, tried pretty much the same trick on an ore called "molybdaena." This name is from a Greek word meaning "lead," because the early chemists mistook the stuff for a lead ore. Hjelm extracted from it a silvery white metal which was certainly not lead. This new metal received the name "molybdenum."

The third of Bergman's element-finding pupils was not Swedish. He was Don Fausto de Elhuyar of Spain. Together with his older brother Don José, he studied a heavy ore called "tungsten" (Swedish for "heavy stone"), or "wolfram." Heating the ore with charcoal, the brothers in 1783 isolated a new element which is called tungsten in the United States and wolfram in Germany.

Bergman had a second-hand connection with still another new metal. In 1782 an Austrian mineralogist, Franz Joseph Müller, separated out of a gold ore a new metal which bore some resemblance to antimony. He sent a sample to Bergman, as the most important mineralogist of the time. Bergman assured him it was not antimony. Eventually this new metal was named tellurium, from a Latin word meaning "earth."

While all these elements were being discovered in Europe, one was also being discovered in the new world. In 1748 a Spanish naval officer named Antonio de Ulloa, traveling in Colombia and Peru on a scientific expedition, came across mines that produced nuggets of a whitish metal. It looked something like silver but was much heavier. The resemblance to silver (for which the Spanish word is "plata") gave the new metal its name—platinum.

Returning to Spain, de Ulloa became a prominent scientist and established the first laboratory in that country devoted to mineralogy. He was also interested in natural history and medicine. In addition, he went to New Orleans as representative of the Spanish king, Charles III, when Spain took over the Louisiana Territory from France after the French and Indian War in America.

Even the old metals known to the alchemists were getting a new going over in these early days of modern chemistry. In 1746 a German chemist, Andreas Sigismund Marggraf, prepared pure zinc and described its properties carefully for the first time; he is therefore listed as the discoverer of the metal.

Marggraf is probably better known, however, for finding sugar in beets. With a microscope, he detected tiny sugar crystals in that vegetable, and thereby gave the world a new source of sugar. Marggraf was the first to use the microscope in chemical research.

As Marggraf had done for zinc, so a French chemist, Claude-François Geoffrey, did for the old metal bismuth. In 1753 he isolated the metal and carefully described its behavior, so he is sometimes given credit for discovering the element.

THE NEW GASES

Metals were not, however, the main interest of the fruitful eighteenth century. The greatest excitement of the time lay in the discovery of new gases. I have already mentioned Boyle's earlier discovery of an inflammable gas through treatment of iron with acid. The man who eventually isolated that gas (hydrogen) was the colorful English chemist Henry Cavendish (1731-1810).

Cavendish was one of the most unusual characters in the history of science. He was eccentric almost to the point of madness. His only interest in life was science. He lived alone, could not bear to speak to more than one person at a time, and could hardly bear even that much. He never married and couldn't look at a woman. Any of his female servants who let herself be seen was fired on the spot. He built a private staircase in his house so that he wouldn't meet anyone by accident while coming or going. He even insisted on dying alone.

As a relative of the Duke of Devonshire, Cavendish inherited a large fortune. He devoted practically all of it to his scientific investigations, continuing to live shabbily on next to nothing.

Cavendish was one of the cleverest experimenters of all

time. He is especially famous for having conducted a delicate measurement of gravitational attraction with small
lead balls which enabled him to calculate the mass of our
planet. He was the first man to "weigh the earth."

In 1776 Cavendish formed a gas, as Boyle had, by the
action of hydrochloric acid on iron, and also by treating
various other metals with acids. The gas in each case was extremely light, much lighter than air itself, and burned
readily with a dim blue flame. Cavendish was certain that
all the samples were the same gas. Because the gas burned
so easily and was so light, Cavendish believed that he had
isolated phlogiston itself.

Meanwhile the composition of air was coming under
closer scrutiny. One of the first to prove that it contained
a mixture of gases was a Scottish chemist, Joseph Black.
He observed that a candle burning in a closed vessel eventually went out. It had exhausted some ingredient of the air
that supported combustion, but there was still air in the
vessel. What was the remaining air made of? Carbon dioxide? Not entirely, for when Black removed the carbon
dioxide by passing the air through a chemical which absorbed that gas, there was still a good deal of air left.

Black suggested to one of his pupils, Daniel Rutherford (who, by the way, was the uncle of Sir Walter Scott),
that he look into the matter. Rutherford did various experiments. He found that a mouse kept in a closed chamber
soon died, apparently having used up some vital gas. Mice
could not live in the remaining air even when the carbon
dioxide was removed from it.

What was this remnant of air, which killed mice and
put out burning candles? Rutherford tried to explain it by
the phlogiston theory. He thought that the air in which
something burned or a mouse breathed became filled with

phlogiston. When air was completely "phlogisticated" (had all the phlogiston it could hold), nothing could burn or live in it.

The "phlogisticated air" that Rutherford prepared was, of course, nitrogen (with traces of the rarer gases in air). So he can be considered the discoverer of nitrogen, though he did not know what the gas was.

A still more exciting discovery was made by an English Unitarian minister named Joseph Priestley (1733-1804). Priestley became interested in science after he met the American scientist and statesman Benjamin Franklin in 1766.

Priestley's church was near a brewery. This establishment gave him an opportunity to study gases, for the fermenting of malt produced bubbles of gas in copious quantities. First he tested the gas to see if it would support combustion. He found that it wouldn't; it quelched smoldering splinters of wood. The gas proved to be carbon dioxide. Priestley dissolved it in water and found that it formed a bubbly water which was tart and pleasant to drink. In other words, we have Priestley to thank for the invention of "soda water," or "seltzer."

His great discovery came from some experiments with mercury. Priestley began by heating mercury with sunlight concentrated through a large magnifying glass. The heat caused the gleaming surface of the mercury to be coated with a reddish powder. He skimmed off the powder and heated it in a test-tube. The powder evaporated into two different gases. One of these vapors then condensed into droplets of mercury; this was simply the original mercury separated from the gas that had turned it into red powder. What, then, was the other gas that had come out of the powder? Priestley collected this gas in a jar and tested it with smoldering splinters of wood. The gas made the smoldering splinters burst into flame! Furthermore, a lighted candle would burn brilliantly in it. And mice placed in the gas became very active. Priestley breathed some of the gas himself and claimed it made him feel very "light and easy."

Thinking about all this in terms of the phlogiston theory, Priestley decided that the gas was "dephlogisticated air"—air with the phlogiston removed. Actually, of course, the gas was pure oxygen.

Priestley's studies unfortunately were cut short by the French Revolution of 1789. He was openly sympathetic to the Revolution, and this was a very unpopular attitude in England, which soon went to war against the French revolutionary government. In 1791 a mob of angry Englishmen burned down Priestley's house in Birmingham. He managed to escape to London and later to the United States, where he had been invited by his old friend, Franklin. Priestley lived in Pennsylvania for the remaining ten years of his life.

Priestley, Rutherford, and Cavendish left the question of the composition of air up in the air, so to speak. As believers in the phlogiston theory, they kept open the possibility that air was a single substance, changing its properties only if it was "phlogisticated" or "dephlogisticated." I will get back to the actual discoveries of the gases that make up air in the next chapter.

HARD-LUCK CHEMIST

So far, the gases I have mentioned are all colorless and odorless—all just like air in appearance. In 1774, however, a colored gas with a choking odor was detected. The man who found it was a Swedish chemist named Karl Wilhelm Scheele (1742-1786). Like Cavendish, he dedicated his life to science and never married.

Scheele was of German descent but lived in Sweden all his life. The seventh child in a family of eleven, he was apprenticed to a pharmacist at the age of 14. In those days pharmacists prepared their own drugs and minerals and often became ardent researchers in chemistry. (In England a pharmacist is still called a "chemist.")

Scheele became the most prolific discoverer of new substances in the history of chemistry. He discovered various mild acids in the plant world (such as tartaric acid, gallic acid, malic acid, citric acid, oxalic acid) and a number of new gases, such as hydrogen sulfide, hydrogen fluoride, and hydrogen cyanide. These gases happened to be very poisonous, but Scheele somehow escaped being killed by them, although he innocently inhaled hydrogen cyanide, for instance, to learn its odor. Scheele also was the first to show that bones contained phosphorous. Among his other discoveries was the compound copper arsenite, which is still known as "Scheele's green."

When it came to the chemical elements, however, Scheele was probably the unluckiest chemist of all time. Time and again he missed credit for a discovery by a hair's breadth.

For instance, he prepared oxygen (in 1771) three years *before* Priestley, and he studied nitrogen before Rutherford. He called oxygen "fire air," because things burned so readily in it, and he called nitrogen "foul air," because it seemed used up so that it would not support combustion. Scheele wrote a description of his experiments and sent the manuscript to a publisher, but the publisher delayed putting the book out for years. By the time it appeared, Rutherford and Priestley had reported their experiments and it was they who got credit for the discoveries.

Scheele also performed experiments which showed the presence of manganese, tungsten, and molybdenum in

minerals. In each case, however, someone else actually isolated the metal and got credit for the discovery. Gahn (the
discoverer of manganese) and Hjelm (the discoverer of
molybdenum) were good friends of Scheele; the de Elhuyar
brothers had visited Scheele before they found tungsten.
But all that Scheele got out of his fruitful studies of minerals
was the naming of one mineral in his honor—"scheelite,"
a mineral from which he first prepared a tungsten compound.

The crowning near-miss, for which he is perhaps best
known, was his discovery of chlorine. In 1774 he treated a
mineral called "pyrolusite" with hydrochloric acid (which
Scheele called "marine acid"). The chemical reaction produced a greenish gas with a choking, unpleasant odor. He
noted that it bleached green leaves and corroded metals.
Scheele thought that the gas was formed by removal of

Table 4

ELEMENTS DISCOVERED IN THE AGE OF PHLOGISTON		
ELEMENT	YEAR DISCOVERED	DISCOVERER
Phosphorus	1669	Brand
Cobalt	1735	Brandt
Platinum	1748	Ulloa
Nickel	1751	Cronstedt
Hydrogen	1766	Cavendish
Nitrogen	1772	Rutherford
Oxygen	1774	Priestley
Chlorine	1774	Scheele
Manganese	1774	Gahn
Molybdenum	1781	Hjelm
Tellurium	1782	Müller
Tungsten	1783	Fausto de Elhuyar / Juan José de Elhuyar

phlogiston from the hydrochloric acid, so he called the gas "dephlogisticated marine acid."

Scheele was clearly the discoverer of this gas, which was later named chlorine, from a Greek word meaning "green." But he did not recognize the gas as an element, and for that reason he is sometimes deprived even of this discovery.

Scheele's hard luck extended to his health. He suffered from severe rheumatic attacks, probably aggravated by his long hours of dedicated night work, and he died at the age of 43.

His death marks the end of the age of phlogiston. In Table 4 I have listed the twelve elements discovered during that period.

6

THE FATHER OF
CHEMISTRY

⇄

One of the reasons the phlogiston theory flourished so long was that chemists paid no attention to the quantitative side of their science. They tinkered with substances, they observed and described their powders and gases carefully— but they did not measure. It didn't matter to them that substances gained or lost weight in surprising ways during their transformations. To the early chemists this seemed of little importance.

Then along came a man who declared that measurement was all-important; it should be the basis of all chemical experiments. This man is now considered the "father of chemistry." He was Antoine Laurent Lavoisier of France (1743-1794).

Lavoisier was born in Paris of well-to-do parents. He had everything. He received an excellent education, first getting a degree in law (his father was a lawyer), then studying astronomy, natural history, and chemistry. Handsome and brilliant, he married a beautiful and intelligent girl with whom he had a happy life. She interested herself in his work and labored by his side.

Surely no happier picture can be imagined. Yet there was a germ of tragedy in Lavoisier's position. His wife was the daughter of one of the chief executives of the *Ferme générale,* a private firm which collected the taxes for Louis XVI's government. Lavoisier himself was a member of this firm. The *Ferme générale* operated on a concession and made a profit of everything it collected above the fixed sum it paid the government. It extorted as much as it could from the tax-paying public, which consisted of the middle-class businessmen and the peasants, the aristocracy being exempt from taxes. The taxpayers, of course, hated the "tax-farmers" even more than they hated the King's government, and when they eventually launched the French Revolution, the *Ferme générale* was one of their main targets.

But before that day of reckoning arrived, Lavoisier put in 20 years of work in science and technology which was of enormous benefit to the French people and to science. He worked out methods of supplying fresh water to Paris and of lighting the streets at night. He helped discover new ways of manufacturing saltpeter, one of the ingredients of gunpowder. Even before he did his main work in chemistry, Lavoisier was admitted at the age of 25 to the *Académie Royale des Sciences,* France's most renowned scientific society.

Soon afterward, in one of his first chemical experiments, Lavoisier demonstrated the importance of measuring things accurately. He repeated a classic experiment which the alchemists had considered clear evidence of the transmutation of an "element." When water, even distilled water, was slowly boiled away in a glass vessel, some sediment was always left in the vessel. This, the alchemists said, showed that some of the water was converted to "earth."

Lavoisier suspected that the real answer was something

else, and he figured out a way to prove his point. He put some rainwater (water that has been distilled by nature) in a clean flask and boiled this water for 101 days. The flask was so designed that all the evaporated water condensed in the upper part of the vessel and dripped back again. Thus the same water evaporated and condensed again and again.

At the end of the 101 days Lavoisier stopped the boiling and let all the water condense. There was quite a bit of sediment in the bottom of the flask. He scraped this out and now weighed the water and the flask separately. He had weighed both, with the most delicate balance he could find, before he started the experiment. Now he found that the water had exactly the same weight as the rainwater he had put in originally. But the *flask* had lost weight! What's more, its loss of weight was exactly equal to the weight of the sediment. There was only one possible answer: the boiling water had dissolved some of the glass. The sediment was not "earth" but simply dissolved glass which came out of solution when the water cooled.

WHY THINGS BURN

Lavoisier's researches into methods of lighting the streets of Paris had led him to consider various lamp fuels and the general nature of combustion. Now he tackled the problem of combustion with his quantitative methods.

He put some tin in a closed vessel and weighed the whole business, vessel and all. Then he heated the vessel. A calx formed on the tin. It was known, as I have mentioned, that the calx of a metal was heavier than the metal itself. Yet when Lavoisier weighed the vessel, he found that the formation of the tin calx had not increased the weight of the vessel's contents. The calx itself, of course, was heavier than the original tin. This meant that it must have gained weight at the expense of something else in the vessel.

When Lavoisier opened the vessel, air rushed in and the system increased in weight. This increase was equal to the extra weight of the calx. So the calx must have taken something from the original air.

This experiment proved a fundamental point which Lavoisier found was true of all chemical reactions: Matter might change its form, but the total weight of the matter involved always remained the same. When a substance gained or lost weight in air, it took something from the air or gave something up to it. This he showed by weighing the whole system, vapors and all. The principle that he demonstrated was later named the "Law of Conservation of Mass."

What did tin take from the air when it formed the calx? Lavoisier decided that it must be Priestley's "dephlogisticated air"—that is, the portion of air that was left after it had been treated to remove the "phlogiston." To test this idea, Lavoisier heated metals in "dephlogisticated air." The metals did indeed absorb all of this gas.

Lavoisier concluded that air consisted of two gases: Priestley's "dephlogisticated air," which Lavoisier now named "oxygen," and Rutherford's "phlogisticated air," which he named "azote." Oxygen came from the Greek words meaning "acid-former"; although Lavoisier was wrong in thinking that oxygen was present in all acids, his name for the gas has stuck ever since. "Azote" he got from the Greek words for "lifeless"; mice, you recall, could not live in "phlogisticated air." But in the English language this gas was later named nitrogen, for the mineral niter, from which it can be prepared.

Lavoisier was able to show that about one-fifth of ordinary air was oxygen and four-fifths nitrogen.

Now Lavoisier produced a new theory of combustion to replace the old phlogiston theory. When a substance burned or tarnished, he said, it combined with oxygen and formed an "oxide." Burning charcoal formed an oxide of carbon (the gas carbon dioxide). A rusting metal formed an oxide ("calx") which had the weight of the metal plus the weight of the oxygen with which it combined. When charcoal was heated with a metal oxide, it restored the original metal not because it added phlogiston but simply because it removed the oxygen from the calx.

Lavoisier published his oxygen theory of combustion in 1783. In the very same year it got a great boost from an experiment by Cavendish, the English genius, who was actually trying to prove something quite opposite. Cavendish, sticking to the phlogiston theory, thought that the "inflammable air" he had prepared was phlogiston. If he added this to "dephlogisticated air," he reasoned, he should get "phlogisticated air." Actually, as we know now, he was proposing to burn hydrogen in oxygen and thereby form nitrogen.

Of course he got nothing of the sort. After burning his "inflammable air" with "dephlogisticated air" and collecting the vapor produced, he found that it condensed into a clear liquid which proved to be water!

Cavendish reported the result very accurately but did not know how to interpret it. As soon as Lavoisier heard about it, he knew the answer, and he confirmed his answer by experiments. Cavendish's "inflammable air," he said, was a gas which he named "hydrogen," from Greek words meaning "water-former." Hydrogen and oxygen combined to form water. Water was the oxide of hydrogen—its "calx," so to speak.

This important experiment at last buried for good the old Greek notions of the elements. It proved that water was not an element but a compound of hydrogen and oxygen, and air was a mixture of nitrogen and oxygen. What's more, it also killed the phlogiston theory quite dead. With these deaths, modern chemistry was born.

If Lavoisier had a fault, it was that he was eager for even more credit than the mountains he deserved. In his accounts of his work he neglected to mention that he knew of Priestley's experiments and had actually discussed Priestley's work with Priestley himself. He let the impression get about that he alone had discovered oxygen. Nor did he make it quite clear that he performed the hydrogen-burning experiment after learning of Cavendish's work.

Priestley and Cavendish may have resented this rather unethical behavior on Lavoisier's part. At all events, neither accepted Lavoisier's oxygen theory of combustion. Both remained convinced of the truth of the phlogiston theory to the day they died. But history has not deprived them of credit for the crucial pioneering experiments that led to the new chemistry.

Oddly enough, alchemy and alchemic frauds lingered on for decades after Lavoisier. The Emperor Francis Joseph of Austria-Hungary, a latter-nineteenth-century medievalist, actually gave money in 1867 to fakers who claimed to be able to manufacture gold from silver and mercury. In fact, there are mystics and cranks even today who believe in alchemy, as some people still believe in astrology, numerology, phrenology and other forms of mysticism.

THE NEW LANGUAGE

Lavoisier's services to chemistry included the coining of a new system for naming chemicals. The alchemists had dressed up their ignorance (or deceit) in fanciful and poetic language. They spoke of gold as the "sun" and of silver as the "moon." To the metal originally known as "quicksilver" or "water-silver" they gave the name of the planet Mercury. They called the mixture of nitric acid and hydrochloric acid, which could dissolve gold, "aqua regia"—a name still sometimes used today.

Chemistry would have been desperately handicapped if it had remained beclouded by the fanciful language of the alchemists. A completely new start had to be made, and Lavoisier, together with a few other French chemists, worked out a new system of chemical nomenclature.

This system is based on the names of the elements and designates compounds according to the elements that make them up. Thus salt, consisting of sodium and chlorine, is called "sodium chloride." The gas made of hydrogen and sulfur is "hydrogen sulfide." An acid containing sulfur is "sulfuric acid." And so on.

The system also has family names for compounds which contain different proportions of a given element. For instance, there is a series of four acids made up of hydrogen, chlorine, and oxygen. Listed in the order of increasing content of oxygen, they are called: (1) hypochlorous acid, (2) chlorous acid, (3) chloric acid, and (4) perchloric acid. If the hydrogen in each acid is replaced by sodium, the resulting compounds are: (1) sodium hypochlorite, (2) sodium chlorite, (3) sodium chlorate, and (4) sodium perchlorate.

The trend to logical nomenclature spread to the elements themselves. Before 1800, elements had been named according to the fancy of the discoverer and without any rules at all. After 1800 it became customary to name all new metallic elements with the ending "um" or "ium," and non-metallic elements with the ending "on" or "ine." With one exception (which I will mention later), all the elements that did not have one of these endings were discovered before Lavoisier's time.

In 1789 Lavoisier published the first modern chemistry text. Its title is *Traité élémentaire de chimie* ("Elementary Textbook of Chemistry"). In this book he discussed all chemical knowledge in the light of his new theory of combustion and used his new nomenclature. He listed the elements named up to that time. Lavoisier's list of 33 "elements" had some curious items. For instance, he included "light" and "caloric" (heat) among his elements. But 23 of his 33 were genuine elements.

Lavoisier's textbook was translated into many languages and spread the new chemistry everywhere. But Lavoisier himself did not live to see its worldwide impact. The year 1789, the year of his book's publication, was also the year of the French Revolution. Lavoisier worked on quietly in his laboratory, avoiding politics, but in 1792 the extremists who had taken over the Revolution finally arrested him as a tax-farmer. Lavoisier protested that he was a scientist, not a tax-farmer. The arresting officer retorted angrily: "The Republic has no need of scientists."

The extremist Jean Paul Marat, who considered himself a scientist, had a strong grudge against Lavoisier, for the chemist had black-balled him when Marat had applied for admission to the *Académie Royale des Sciences*. Marat personally saw to it that Lavoisier was condemned to the guillotine. Marat himself was assassinated soon after the verdict, but on May 2, 1794, Lavoisier was beheaded anyway.

Ironically, only ten weeks later sanity returned to France and the extremists were overthrown. The execution of Lavoisier remains the greatest single tragedy of the Revolution. Science and chemistry certainly lost a great deal by his death at the still fruitful age of 50.

7

THE INVISIBLE
PARTICLES

಄

Lavoisier's new chemistry made more puzzling than ever the old question: what *was* an element, after all? What made one distinct from another? Here was a long and growing list of elements, many possessing certain common properties, and yet each with its own unchangeable character. For example, iron, cobalt, and nickel were very much alike in some ways, but iron couldn't be changed into nickel or cobalt, any more than lead could be changed to gold. Hydrogen, nitrogen, and oxygen were all colorless gases, but all three behaved very differently when heated, and no amount of violent treatment could transform one into another.

Within two decades after Lavoisier's death, the mystery of the immutability of the elements was solved. Actually the key to the whole business had been guessed by a few inspired Greeks more than 2,000 years earlier.

The Greek philosopher Anaxagoras seems to have been the first to suggest that all matter was made up of tiny particles. Leucippus of Miletus was intrigued by the

53

idea and discussed it with his pupil Democritus (not to be confused with the later alchemist Bolos Democritus).

Democritus developed the thought further. He was born in a little Aegean town called Abdera. The Greeks considered Abdera a typical hick town, and "Abderite" came to mean a stupid country fellow. Democritus was one Abderite who turned out to be anything but stupid. He became one of the foremost philosophers of Greece. (He was called the "Laughing Philosopher," by the way, because of his cheerful outlook.)

Democritus decided that invisibly small particles made up each element, and that the nature of the element depended on the shape of its particles. Thus water might be made of smooth spheres, which would explain why water flowed so easily; the particles of "earth" might be cubes, which would account for the hardness and stability of that "element;" the particles of "fire" were sharp and pointed, which was why fire hurt. From these few types of particles, Democritus said, all the known substances might be built.

He called the little particles "atoms" (from a Greek word meaning indivisible) because he held that they could not be destroyed or broken down into anything smaller.

Unfortunately Democritus' theory was ridiculed by Aristotle, the most influential of all the ancient philosophers. Furthermore, the writings of Democritus were lost, so his ideas were preserved only in the form of occasional critical references to them by other philosophers.

Still, the theory of atoms did not die. Epicurus of Samos championed Democritus' view. In the last century B.C., the Roman philosopher Lucretius, an Epicurean, revived the atomic theory in his famous *De rerum natura* ("On the Nature of Things"). Lucretius' book, written in Latin, remained influential throughout the Middle Ages. And so was a book by a third-century Greek natural philosopher named Hero; his work, called *Pneumatica* ("About Air"), described experiments with air and explained the results in terms of the theory that air was made up of atoms.

Then in the seventeenth century Robert Boyle's experiments advanced support for the theory when he showed that a given amount of air could be compressed into a smaller and smaller volume with increasing pressure. This certainly indicated that air was made up of particles surrounded by empty space.

Through the seventeenth and eighteenth centuries "atomism" aroused more and more interest. The great Isaac Newton believed in the existence of atoms. But evidence of their existence did not come forth until chemists began to study substances by the weighing methods introduced by Lavoisier.

In 1797 Joseph Louis Proust, a Frenchman who was working in Spain, arrived at an important discovery from weighing compounds. He found that elements always combined in certain definite proportions by weight. For instance, in copper carbonate, a compound of copper, carbon, and oxygen, the proportions by weight were always five parts of copper, four parts of oxygen, and one part of carbon—that is, 5 to 4 to 1.

Proust's "law of definite proportions" was the first specific confirmation of the atomic idea. If matter was made of indivisible building blocks, this was exactly what you would expect to find: elements should combine in a whole-number ratio, such as five to one or four to one—never five and a quarter or four and a half to one, because you couldn't have a fraction of an atom.

Then came a further observation which really established the atomic theory. The man who took that step, and formulated the theory in meaningful terms, was John Dalton of England (1766-1844).

Dalton was a Quaker schoolmaster in a small English town. He became a science buff who interested himself in all the sciences. Among other things, he built instruments to study the weather, kept careful daily weather records for 46 years, and wrote a book which entitles him to be considered one of the founders of the science of meteorology. Another of his achievements was the discovery of color-blindness, still sometimes called "Daltonism" in his honor. Dalton was color-blind himself. But that handicap did not prevent him from taking up chemistry and making his greatest discovery.

Dalton started from Proust's law of definite proportions. He was particularly struck by the fact that two elements could combine in more than one way. For instance, there were two different oxides of carbon: carbon dioxide and carbon monoxide (of course, the gases were not known by those names then). In carbon dioxide, the proportion of oxygen to carbon by weight was 8 to 3; in carbon monoxide it was 4 to 3. In other words, the proportion of oxygen in the first compound was exactly twice that in the second. Dalton called this discovery the "law of multiple proportions."

Now what did it mean? Taking the case of the carbon oxides, what else could it mean except that carbon dioxide had two atoms of oxygen to one of carbon and carbon monoxide had one of oxygen to one of carbon?

Dalton thereupon (in 1803) set forth the atomic theory, working it out for the first time in rational detail. Each element consisted of a particular kind of atom. The atoms of the various elements differed in weight. Since in the one-carbon-one-oxygen compound (carbon monoxide) the proportion of carbon to oxygen by weight was 3 to 4, the carbon atom must be three-fourths the weight of the oxygen atom. In this way Dalton worked out the relative weights of a number of elements. He decided that the chief distinction between the different elements was the difference in their atomic weight.

Here was a reasonable explanation of why lead couldn't be changed into gold, or iron into cobalt, or hydrogen into nitrogen. To change one element to another you would have to change atoms of one weight into atoms of another weight—a thing which was impossible to accomplish by chemistry (and was achieved only by nuclear physics in the twentieth century).

Dalton published his atomic theory in a book titled *New System of Chemical Philosophy*. His "new system" met resistance, but many chemists accepted it at once.

Why was it that they now suddenly took up Dalton's view with enthusiasm, whereas for thousands of years scientists had not taken seriously Democritus' suggestion of much the same idea? Well, the whole background had changed. Now there was nearly a century and a half of detailed observation and experiments to back up Dalton's interpretation. He showed that the atomic theory could explain all the observations and measurements.

A VARIETY OF "EARTHS"

The discovery of new elements speeded up. It had been accelerating even before Dalton expounded his theory. One of the most active discoverers was a German chemist named Martin Heinrich Klaproth (1743-1817). Like Scheele, Klaproth started as an apprentice to a pharmacist. He became a great authority on minerals and a professor of chemistry at the University of Berlin.

In 1789, the year of the publication of Lavoisier's textbook, Klaproth was investigating a dark, heavy mineral found in an old Bohemian mine. He dissolved the mineral in strong acid, then neutralized the acid. A yellow powder settled out. Klaproth decided, correctly, that this was an oxide of a new metal.

Taking his cue from the alchemists who had named elements after planets, Klaproth named this metal for Uranus, which had been discovered in the sky just eight years before. So the new element was called "uranium." In the same year Klaproth extracted the oxide of another new metal from a semi-precious stone called zircon, and he named this element "zirconium." *

Klaproth was a man who had no desire for any credit that was not his own. He noted that in 1782 Franz Joseph Müller had discovered a new element which had been neglected and not yet even given a name (see Chapter 5). Klaproth called it to the attention of the scientific world and named the element tellurium ("earth"). He was careful to point out that the credit for the discovery belonged to Müller.

He did the same on behalf of an English clergyman named William Gregor, who in 1791 discovered the oxide of a new metal in a black sand he found in his own parish. Gregor's description went unnoticed until Klaproth drew attention to it. He again suggested a name for the element— "titanium" (after the Titans of Greek mythology)—and gave credit to Gregor as the discoverer.

Virtue brings its rewards. Lavoisier never received the credit as an element-finder for which he hungered. Klaproth, on the other hand, who did his best to avoid unearned credit, is nevertheless often listed as the discoverer of tellurium and titanium.

---

* Ordinarily, credit for the discovery of an element goes to the man who first isolates the element itself. A number of times, however, it has gone to the man who first purified the oxide and showed that it must contain a new element. Klaproth never isolated uranium (though he thought he did) or zirconium. In fact, neither metal was obtained in reasonable purity until the twentieth century.

The oxides of uranium, zirconium, and titanium were called "earths," because they were insoluble in water and not affected by heat. In 1794 a particularly interesting new "earth" was discovered in a mineral obtained from a rock quarry in the little town of Ytterby in Sweden. It found its way into the hands of a Finnish chemist named Johan Gadolin, another of the pupils of Bergman (see Chapter 5). Gadolin called the new mineral "yttria," after the town, and the metal itself was eventually named "yttrium." Gadolin gets credit for its discovery.

This new "earth" was fairly uncommon, and was therefore called a "rare earth." Soon other "rare-earth" elements turned up.

A Swedish boy of 15 named Wilhelm Hisinger found an interesting mineral on his father's estate and sent it to Scheele for analysis. Poor, hard-luck Scheele found nothing unusual in it, but Hisinger kept up his interest in the mineral and eventually, at the age of 37, showed that it contained a new element. This was named "cerium," for an asteroid, Ceres, which had been discovered in 1801.

In 1798 a French chemist, Louis Nicolas Vauquelin, was analyzing a mineral which had been discovered in Siberia. He obtained from it beautiful red and yellow compounds that turned to bright green when certain chemicals were added. From these compounds he extracted the oxide of a new metal, and by heating the oxide with charcoal, he isolated bits of the metal itself. He called it chromium, from the Greek word for "color."

The following year Vauquelin discovered an oxide of still another new metal in a semi-precious gem called beryl. This metal was eventually named beryllium.

About the same time, America contributed a new element. Before the Revolution, the colonial governor had sent to London an unusual mineral found in Connecticut.

In 1801 an English chemist, Charles Hatchett, chipped off a piece of the specimen and analyzed it. He decided that it contained a new metal and he named this "columbium," after Columbia, the poetic nickname of the new nation of the United States. Some years later the English chemist William Hyde Wollaston, after analyzing a second piece, declared that "columbium" was actually the same as the element "tantalum," which had been discovered by a Swedish chemist, Anders Gustaf Ekeberg, and named for Tantalus, a character in the Greek myths.

The issue was finally settled in 1846 by a German chemist, Heinrich Rose, who showed that Hatchett was right and Wollaston was wrong. Columbium was very similar to tantalum, but not identical with it. Because of its similarity to tantalum, Rose renamed columbium "niobium," after Niobe, the daughter of Tantalus. For many years Europeans called the element niobium and Americans called it columbium, but niobium is now the official name.

Wollaston made up for his mistake by unearthing some genuine discoveries. He liked to work with the minerals of platinum, a fascinating metal. Like gold it was a "noble metal"—that is, it formed compounds only reluctantly and therefore did not tarnish or rust. It wasn't as beautiful as gold (no metal is), but it was rarer and more expensive.

Like gold, platinum could be dissolved in "aqua regia." But it turned out that some impurities in its mineral were also dissolved with it. Wollaston separated these impurities, and in 1803 he discovered two lighter metals which were similar in behavior to platinum but not so "noble." He called them "palladium" and "rhodium"— palladium in honor of a newly discovered planetoid, Pallas, and rhodium from a Greek word meaning "rose-red," because the element formed compounds of that color.

Another English chemist, Smithson Tennant (for

whom Wollaston had once worked as an assistant), found two other metals with platinum, but these were more "noble" than platinum. They were not soluble in aqua regia. Tennant named them "osmium" and "iridium." Osmium came from the Greek word for "odor"—one of the element's compounds had an unpleasant aroma. Iridium was named from the Greek word for "rainbow," for the colorfulness of its compounds.

Summing up this chapter, I have listed in Table 5 the elements discovered around the turn of the nineteenth century.

Table 5

ELEMENTS DISCOVERED IN THE TIME OF DALTON

Element	Year Discovered	Discoverer
Uranium	1789	Klaproth
Zirconium	1789	Klaproth
Titanium	1791	Gregor
Yttrium	1794	Gadolin
Beryllium	1798	Vauquelin
Chromium	1798	Vauquelin
Niobium (Columbium)	1801	Hatchett
Tantalum	1802	Ekeberg
Rhodium	1803	Wollaston
Palladium	1803	Wollaston
Cerium	1803	Hisinger
Osmium	1804	Tennant
Iridium	1804	Tennant

8

DISCOVERIES WITH ELECTRICITY

Lavoisier's list of 33 "elements" included several substances which some chemists believed were compounds. These were "lime," "magnesia," "baryta," "alumina," and "silica."

Lime is the English word for what the Romans had originally called "calx." It was formed by heating limestone. Magnesia was named for the Greek city near which it was first discovered, according to legend. Baryta, obtained from a very heavy mineral, was from a Greek word meaning "heavy." Alumina came from a common mineral called "alumen," and silica from flint, called "silex" by the Romans.

Lavoisier considered all these to be elements because they could not be reduced by heating them with charcoal. But other chemists suspected that they were really oxides, and they looked for some other way to pry the oxygen loose and find the central elements. They succeeded in finding a way—electricity.

At the time, electricity was a very exciting and popular

new toy. Benjamin Franklin had drawn electricity from a thundercloud with his famous kite. Alessandro Volta of Italy had just invented his electric battery (in 1800). The news of this work ran through the scientific world with an effect as electrifying as that of his currents.

In England, a scientist named William Nicholson and his young friend Anthony Carlisle at once started chemical experiments with electricity. They stuck two electrodes from a battery in some slightly acidified water, and found that the electric current passing through the water caused bubbles of gas to appear at each electrode. The gas turned out to be oxygen at one electrode and hydrogen at the other. In short, electricity broke down water into hydrogen and oxygen—two parts of hydrogen to one part of oxygen. (Dalton, in working out his atomic theory, made the mistake of supposing that water contained one atom of hydrogen to one of oxygen, and consequently many of his atomic weights were incorrect.)

The Nicholson-Carlisle experiment showed that electricity could pull the elements of a compound apart. Great things soon came from this demonstration.

DAVY HITS THE JACKPOT

Two young chemists led the way. They were Jöns Jakob Berzelius of Sweden (1779-1848) and Humphry Davy of England (1778-1829).

Berzelius, brought up by a stepfather, had a hard childhood but eventually went to medical school and won his degree. He was not, however, very interested in medical studies. What did interest him was experimenting in chemistry. Under the guidance of his teacher (a nephew of the great Bergman) he took up research in that field and became the most important chemist of his time.

As a professor of chemistry, Berzelius was a powerful

lecturer. Students flocked to him from all over Europe. His views in every branch of chemistry became almost law—even though he was often wrong. In the history of chemistry, the first half of the nineteenth century might be called the "Age of Berzelius."

Berzelius published a textbook in chemistry (in 1808) which replaced Lavoisier's as the prime authority on the subject. For almost 30 years he also published an annual report on chemical progress. In his late years, as the elder statesman of chemistry, conservative Professor Berzelius usually managed to come out on the wrong side of most controversies over new theories. But right or wrong, throughout his life he was a stimulating force in the whole exciting world of chemistry.

One of his first contributions was to suggest, after repeating the Nicholson-Carlisle experiment, that the elements carried charges of electricity. From this he evolved a theory of chemical reactions which was widely accepted but which proved wrong. However, the idea of electrical charges on atoms was found to be correct nearly a century later.

Humphry Davy also started as a child of poverty. Like so many other chemists of the time, he began as a pharmacist's apprentice. He became interested in chemistry after reading Lavoisier's textbook. In 1799, when he was only 21, he suddenly found himself famous because he discovered something called "laughing gas."

This gas is nitrous oxide, a compound of two atoms of nitrogen and one of oxygen. No sooner had Davy prepared it than it was found to have astonishing properties. People who breathed nitrous oxide seemed to lose control of themselves. Their emotions flowed unchecked; they laughed, cried, and generally behaved foolishly. Breathing the drug became a great fad. (Not until many years later did medical men adopt it as an anesthetic, for pulling teeth and other minor surgery.)

On the strength of his discovery, Davy became a popular public lecturer on chemistry. Science was all the rage. The new steam engine and balloon flights were the talk of the day, as rockets and astronauts are now. Davy was handsome, an excellent speaker, and skilled in spectacular demonstrations with electricity and other wonders of the new science. Throngs came to hear him.

But Davy was less interested in lecturing than in working in the laboratory. What about using electricity to break down tightly bound compounds that the chemists had failed to separate?

Davy first tackled the substance known as "potash." This was literally an ash, obtained by burning certain plants and then steeping the ashes in water in a large pot. Davy began by running an electric current through a solution of potash. All he got was hydrogen and oxygen, from the breakdown of the water. He decided he would have to perform the experiment in the absence of water. So he melted some dry potash and ran the current through the hot melt. To do this he had to build huge batteries capable of delivering far stronger currents than Volta's original small one.

At once, shiny globules appeared at one of the platinum electrodes. Davy was sure this metallic substance was a new element. He called it "potassium" (from potash). He found that potassium was extremely active chemically and would react with almost any substance. In water, for instance, it snatched at the oxygen atoms and liberated hydrogen with such energy that the hydrogen caught fire.

A few days later Davy tried the same trick with soda, also a product obtained by burning plants. From soda he isolated "sodium," an element very like potassium.

The Arabs had called soda and potash *al-qili* (meaning "the ash"). That is why those substances are referred to as "alkalis" and potassium and sodium are known as alkali metals.

After isolating these elements, Davy proceeded to try to break down some of Lavoisier's "elements," beginning with lime. He got nowhere at first. But at this point Berzelius came to the rescue. Berzelius had found that when he added a mercury compound to lime or baryta and sent a current through, he got an "amalgam" of mercury and some other metal. He wrote to Davy telling about his results. That gave Davy a fresh start. He prepared the amalgams and then heated them strongly.

The trick worked. From the amalgam derived from lime he isolated a metal which he named "calcium" (after "calx"). From Baryta he got "barium," and from magnesia he isolated "magnesium." He went on to give the same treatment to a mineral named after the small Scottish town of Strontian, and from this he separated another new metallic element—"strontium."

All these elements are now known as "alkaline-earth metals."

DAVY WINS AND LOSES

Davy can be connected with two other elements.

In 1810 he reported experiments which seemed to show that the green gas Scheele had obtained from hydrochloric acid was an element, not a compound as Scheele had thought. Davy named it "chlorine" for its green color. For years Berzelius and the French chemists Joseph Louis Gay-Lussac and Louis Jacques Thénard denied that chlorine was an element. But Gay-Lussac and Thénard failed in their efforts to split it into simpler substances. (Gay-Lussac, by the way, went four miles high in a balloon in 1804 to test the composition of the air at great heights. He was one of the first important scientists to venture into the third dimension in this way.)

The issue was finally resolved indirectly through the discovery of an element like chlorine by another French chemist, Bernard Courtois. He was experimenting with the ashes of burned seaweed, a good source of sodium and potassium. Treating the ashes with strong acid to remove sulfur compounds, Courtois one day noticed that a violet vapor came out. This cooled to dark crystals of a new substance. He decided that it was an element, and he named it "iodine," from the Greek word for "violet."

Now iodine proved to be very similar chemically to chlorine. If iodine was an element, in all likelihood chlorine was also. This reasoning convinced Berzelius.

In 1826 there came a further discovery which clinched the matter. A French chemist named Antoine Jérôme Balard, working with salts precipitated from sea water, found that the addition of certain chemicals turned them brown. He tracked down the brown color to a new element with a strong and unpleasant odor. Balard named it "bromine," from the Greek word for "stench."

Bromine, iodine, and chlorine all form similar compounds; for instance, the salts of bromine and iodine are very much like sodium chloride. For that reason, all three elements are called "halogens," from Greek words meaning "salt-formers."

Gay-Lussac and Thénard won out over Davy, however, in another contest. For many years chemists had tried to isolate a new element from borax. Lavoisier was so sure that its acid, boric acid, contained such an element that he included the "boric radical" in his list of elements. In 1808 Gay-Lussac and Thénard decided to take a leaf out of Davy's book in going after this element.

Davy had shown that potassium atoms gripped oxygen very tightly. They must have a stronger affinity for oxygen than carbon atoms did, because heating potash with charcoal failed to separate the potassium from the oxygen. So Gay-Lussac and Thénard tried heating boric acid with potassium, with the idea that since potassium had such an affinity for oxygen, it might seize and remove the oxygen where carbon had failed. (Napoleon Bonaparte, by the way, financed their experiments, because he wanted a scientific victory over England, with which France was at war at the time. Scientific rivalry between nations for propaganda purposes, you see, is not a new phenomenon of our time.)

The Frenchmen scored a victory. Their experiment produced the new element "boron." Davy independently was trying the same tactics and also isolated boron, but he was exactly nine days later than the French.

BERZELIUS JOINS THE HUNT

Meanwhile Berzelius also was becoming active in the element-hunting game. He had a number of near-misses. Davy beat him to the discovery of barium and calcium. Berzelius worked for a time with Hisinger and came close to sharing the credit for discovering cerium, but Hisinger accomplished this by himself later. One of Berzelius' pupils, named Johan August Arfvedson, also found an element independently. Young Arfvedson decided that a certain Swedish mineral must contain a chemically active metal similar to the alkali metals (sodium and potassium) that had been found in plants. He named the new one lithium, from the Greek word for "rock." Arfvedson didn't succeed in isolating lithium, but Davy did later.

In 1817, the same year that Arfvedson found lithium,

one of Vauquelin's students, a German chemist named Friedrich Stromeyer, separated a new metal similar to zinc from a mineral called "cadmia." He named the element cadmium.

Berzelius himself finally graduated to being a discoverer in his own right. He was bound to sooner or later, for he had a finger in every pie. In 1818 he was analyzing samples of some sulfuric acid prepared in a Swedish mining town, and he found an impurity which he believed was a new metal. He thought at first it might be tellurium, but when he isolated the metal, it turned out to be something else—a new element that resembled tellurium. Because tellurium had been named for the earth, Berzelius named the new element "selenium," from the Greek word for the moon.

In 1824 Berzelius tackled silica, one earth on Lavoisier's list of elements which Davy had not broken down. Adopting the method of Gay-Lussac and Thénard, Berzelius heated silica with potassium. He succeeded in isolating the element silicon.

That left the last "earth" on Lavoisier's list—alumina. Davy and Berzelius both tried to isolate it by electrical means, without success. But in 1827 a pupil of Berzelius, Friedrich Wöhler, managed to extract a small quantity of metal, albeit impure, from this oxide. This metal, of course, was aluminum. An electrical method for purifying aluminum on a substantial scale was not worked out until 1886, four years after Wöhler's death.

Berzelius was to add a third element to his own list of discoveries. In 1829, in a mineral sent him by a Norwegian minister, he found a metal which he named "thorium," after the old Norse god Thor.

One year later a Berzelius pupil, Nils Gabriel Sefström, discovered another new metal in a sample of iron ore, and he, too, named it after an old Norse deity. He chose a goddess, Vanadis, and called the element "vanadium."

In Table 6 I list the elements discovered in the quarter century dominated by Davy and Berzelius.

Table 6

ELEMENTS DISCOVERED IN THE TIME OF DAVY AND BERZELIUS

Element	Year Discovered	Discoverer
Potassium	1807	Davy
Sodium	1807	Davy
Magnesium	1808	Davy
Calcium	1808	Davy
Strontium	1808	Davy
Barium	1808	Davy
Boron	1808	{ Gay-Lussac { Thénard
Iodine	1811	Courtois
Lithium	1817	Arfvedson
Cadmium	1817	Stromeyer
Selenium	1818	Berzelius
Silicon	1824	Berzelius
Bromine	1826	Balard
Aluminum	1827	Wöhler
Thorium	1829	Berzelius
Vanadium	1830	Sefström

9

SYMBOLS AND
WEIGHTS

By 1830 Thales' original question, What is the universe made of? had reaped a bewildering harvest of answers. Looking for the single basic building material of the universe, chemists had already found 54 different elements! And there was no telling how many more awaited discovery. Chemistry was becoming a jungle.

With all those elements, and the vast number of compounds that could be made from them, the chemists had to devise some shorthand system for labeling them; otherwise they would be lost in a great tangle of long names.

The alchemists had invented symbols for their elements, but these were cabalistic signs, taken from astrology, which merely made chemistry more mysterious. For instance, gold was ☉, silver was ☽, copper was ♀, iron was ♂.

In the eighteenth century Etienne François Geoffroy added more occult symbols for elements and compounds— a small crown for antimony, a triangle pointing up for sulfur, a cross with four dots for vinegar, and so on.

This sort of language was meaningless and hard to

remember. When Dalton proposed his theory of atoms (which he pictured as tiny spheres) he tried to simplify things by representing each element by a circle with a distinguishing mark: oxygen was a white circle, carbon was a black one, hydrogen a circle with a dot in it, nitrogen one with a vertical line through it; other elements had an initial in the circle, such as "s" for sulfur, "g" for gold, and so on.

It was Berzelius who finally came up with a rational system. Why not simply use the initial letter of each element's name as its symbol? (To get around language differences—*e.g.*, nitrogen was "nitrogen" in English, "azote" in French, and "Stickstoff" in German—he took the Latin names as the universal language. Fortunately for those of us who speak English, most of the English names and initials are the same as in Latin.)

So oxygen became O, hydrogen H, nitrogen N, carbon C, and so on. Where more than one element had the same initial letter, a second letter was used to avoid confusion, thus: Ca for calcium, Cd for cadmium, Cl for chlorine.

The new shorthand showed the composition of a compound at a glance. CO_2 (carbon dioxide) says that the molecule has one atom of carbon and two of oxygen. Likewise, H_2O, NH_3, $CaSO_4$, and all other expressions in this form are easy to read and uniquely define the compounds.

Berzelius' logical system naturally was promptly adopted, and it has stood up ever since.

In Tables 7 and 8 I list the 54 elements known in 1830 and their symbols. The reason for the two tables is merely to show that some of the symbols (in Table 8) stand for Latin names which are not the same in English. For instance, Na, for sodium, comes from the latin *natrium;* Au, for gold, is from *aurum;* Fe, for iron, from *ferrum,* etc.

WEIGHING THE ATOMS

Chemistry owes one further great debt to Berzelius. After creating a language for the elements, he proceeded to establish their atomic weights on a firm foundation.

Table 7

SYMBOLS OF ELEMENTS

ELEMENT	SYMBOL	ELEMENT	SYMBOL
Aluminum	Al	Niobium	Nb
Arsenic	As	Nitrogen	N
Barium	Ba	Osmium	Os
Beryllium	Be	Oxygen	O
Bismuth	Bi	Palladium	Pd
Boron	B	Phosphorus	P
Bromine	Br	Platinum	Pt
Cadmium	Cd	Rhodium	Rh
Calcium	Ca	Selenium	Se
Carbon	C	Silicon	Si
Cerium	Ce	Strontium	Sr
Chlorine	Cl	Sulfur	S
Chromium	Cr	Tantalum	Ta
Cobalt	Co	Tellurium	Te
Hydrogen	H	Thorium	Th
Iodine	I	Titanium	Ti
Iridium	Ir	Uranium	U
Lithium	Li	Vanadium	V
Magnesium	Mg	Yttrium	Y
Manganese	Mn	Zinc	Zn
Molybdenum	Mo	Zirconium	Zr
Nickel	Ni		

Dalton had tried to work out the atomic weights but got many of them quite wrong because he was a clumsy worker. Berzelius spent many years painstakingly analyzing thousands of compounds and weighing exactly how much of each element they contained. As the standard for the relative weights of the elements he eventually took the

Table 8

SYMBOLS FROM LATIN NAMES

ENGLISH NAME	LATIN NAME	SYMBOL
Antimony	Stibium	Sb
Copper	Cuprum	Cu
Gold	Aurum	Au
Iron	Ferrum	Fe
Lead	Plumbum	Pb
Mercury	Hydrargyrum	Hg
Potassium	Kalium	K
Silver	Argentum	Ag
Sodium	Natrium	Na
Tin	Stannum	Sn
Tungsten	Wolframium	W

weight of hydrogen as equal to 1 and measured all the others as multiples of that unit. Later chemists found that they got more precise values if they used oxygen, at an atomic weight of exactly 16, as the standard. (Very recently they have switched to carbon-12, the carbon isotope with an atomic weight of 12, as the most precise available standard, and the table of atomic weights has been recalculated on that basis.)

By 1826 Berzelius had prepared a list of atomic weights which even twentieth-century chemists would consider pretty good. All but three of his weights were just about correct. The three he had wrong were silver, sodium, and potassium; his figures for those were about twice what they should be. All in all, his measurements were an incredible feat of skill and hard work.

Table 9

ATOMIC WEIGHTS

ELEMENT	ATOMIC WEIGHT	ELEMENT	WEIGHT ATOMIC
Aluminum	26.98	Nickel	58.71
Antimony	121.76	Niobium	92.91
Arsenic	74.91	Nitrogen	14.008
Barium	137.36	Osmium	190.2
Beryllium	9.013	Oxygen	16.0000
Bismuth	209.00	Palladium	106.4
Boron	10.82	Phosphorus	30.975
Bromine	79.916	Platinum	195.09
Cadmium	112.41	Potassium	39.100
Calcium	40.08	Rhodium	102.91
Carbon	12.011	Selenium	78.96
Cerium	140.13	Silicon	28.09
Chlorine	35.457	Silver	107.88
Chromium	52.01	Sodium	22.991
Cobalt	58.94	Strontium	87.63
Copper	63.54	Sulfur	32.066
Gold	197.0	Tantalum	180.95
Hydrogen	1.0080	Tellurium	127.61
Iodine	126.91	Thorium	232.05
Iridium	192.2	Tin	118.70
Iron	55.85	Titanium	47.90
Lead	207.21	Tungsten	183.86
Lithium	6.940	Uranium	238.07
Magnesium	24.32	Vanadium	50.95
Manganese	54.94	Yttrium	88.92
Mercury	200.61	Zinc	65.38
Molybdenum	95.95	Zirconium	91.22

To be sure, chemists since then have done a lot of correcting and refining of Berzelius' figures, developing ever more delicate methods for their measurements. To take one example: Berzelius found the sulfur atom to be twice as heavy as the oxygen atom, which gave sulfur an atomic weight of 32. Some 70 years later, chemists placed its weight at 32.06. In 1925 they pushed the measurement another decimal place to 32.064. In 1956 they corrected this to 32.066. But you see how close to the mark Berzelius came.

In Table 9 I list the 54 elements known in his time with their atomic weights, on the basis of oxygen at 16.0000. These weights are close to Berzelius' in almost every case.

Once the atomic weights are known, the relative weights of individual molecules can be calculated easily. For instance, the "molecular weight" of sodium carbonate, Na_2CO_3, is the sum of two sodium atoms (22.991 plus 22.991), a carbon atom (12.011), and three oxygen atoms (16.0000 plus 16.0000 plus 16.0000), all of which adds up to 105.993.

THE CONGRESS AT KARLSRUHE

Oddly enough, most chemists of his time did not think much of Berzelius' list of atomic weights. Atoms were small, invisible, intangible; how could one be sure of how much they weighed? The chemists preferred to calculate in terms of their direct measurements of substances as they handled them. For instance, they found that water contained eight parts of oxygen to one part of hydrogen by weight. So they said the "equivalent weight" of oxygen was 8. This seemed to them to make more sense than saying the atomic weight of oxygen was 16.

However, many chemists fell into the habit of confusing equivalent weight with atomic weight and often listed the atomic weight of oxygen as 8. Moreover, they were not too careful about distinguishing between "atomic weight" and "molecular weight."

As a result of all this, frequent disagreements arose as to how to write the formulas of the more complicated molecules, particularly those in which carbon was involved. With one chemist saying a molecule should have two oxygen atoms with a weight of 8 each, and another saying it should have one oxygen atom with a weight of 16, you can see where an awful lot of energy was wasted in useless fighting.

Finally one of the most important chemists of the day, Friedrich August Kekule of Germany, proposed: Why not call a conference of important chemists from all over Europe and discuss the matter?

So the First International Chemical Congress (as it was called) met in 1860 in the town of Karlsruhe in the little kingdom of Baden, just across the Rhine from France. It got off on the wrong foot. The chemists talked and talked and seemed to be getting nowhere. Then an Italian chemist named Stanislao Cannizzaro suddenly changed the whole spirit of the meeting.

Cannizzaro was a fiery man used to controversy. He had taken an active part in a revolution against Naples in his native Sicily and left in a hurry when the revolution lost. Working and biding his time in France and Egypt, he had returned to Italy in 1860 when the new kingdom of a united Italy was being formed. (Cannizzaro later became vice president of the Italian Senate.) Now, in the midst of this turmoil, Cannizzaro had taken time out to go to the Congress at Karlsruhe.

Facing the disputing chemists, Cannizzaro electrified the assemblage with a fiery defense of the atomic approach in chemistry. Let us put an end, he pleaded, to confusion between atoms and molecules, between equivalent weights and atomic weights. By concentrating on atomic weights, one could clarify their formulas and bring order out of chaos.

Cannizzaro convinced the chemists. They went back to their laboratories with a new confidence and began to work in a more systematic way with more fruitful results.

Meanwhile more new elements had been turning up.

One of Berzelius' favorite assistants, Carl Gustav Mosander, had analyzed a rare-earth called ceria (cerium oxide). From his sample of the mineral he dissolved, with strong acid, a new oxide. At Berzelius' suggestion Mosander called it "lanthana" (from the Greek for "hidden"), because it had been hidden in the mineral. It was the oxide of a new element, which naturally was named "lanthanum."

Two years later Mosander isolated another oxide from his preparation. This metal was so like lanthanum that he called it "didymium" (Greek for "twin"). Actually didymium was not an element at all but a mixture of two almost identical elements—twins indeed. This was not discovered, however, until 40 years later, long after Mosander's death.

Mosander turned to the rare-earth "yttria." After two more years of work, he showed that yttria could be separated into three oxides. One, possessing the characteristic properties of yttria, was colorless. The other two were a yellow oxide which he named "erbia" and a rose-colored one he named "terbia." The metals were, correspondingly, "erbium" and "terbium." So three elements—yttrium, erbium, and terbium—all got their names from the little hamlet of Ytterby.

I mentioned at the end of Chapter 7 that the platinum-bearing ores had yielded five elements—platinum, osmium, iridium, palladium, and rhodium. In 1844 a sixth "platinum metal" was discovered. Karl Karlovich Klaus, an Estonian-born orphan of German ancestry, apprenticed himself to a pharmacist and eventually managed to get a job as a pharmacist in the Volga steppes, where he spent years studying the plant and animal life. Then he went into mineralogical research and began to study platinum ores in the Ural Mountains. He was deliberately hunting for new metals in them. One by one he separated each of the five known platinum metals, and at last he found a sixth, rarer than any of the other five. He named it "ruthenium," after an old name for Russia.

Table 10 lists the elements discovered during Berzelius' final decade of life.

Table 10

ELEMENTS DISCOVERED IN BERZELIUS' LAST YEARS				
ELEMENT	SYMBOL	ATOMIC WEIGHT	YEAR DISCOVERED	DISCOVERER
Lanthanum	La	138.92	1839	Mosander
Erbium	Er	167.27	1843	Mosander
Terbium	Tb	158.93	1843	Mosander
Ruthenium	Ru	101.1	1844	Klaus

By the time of the First International Chemical Congress at Karlsruhe, then, the number of known elements had reached 58.

10

CLUES IN THE
SPECTRUM

After the Congress of Karlsruhe, atomic weights became a big factor in the search for the elements, as well as in chemists' everyday work. It seemed that atomic weight might shed light on the resemblances and differences among the elements and might even lead to the discovery of new ones.

Here, for instance, were cobalt and nickel. Cobalt's atomic weight is 58.94, and nickel's is 58.71. The two elements closely resemble each other. Perhaps this meant that the closer two elements were in atomic weight, the more alike they would be.

The trouble with this theory was that it just didn't work. Copper and zinc are very close together in atomic weight—63.54 and 65.38, respectively. Yet these two metals are not at all alike. Or consider sulfur (atomic weight: 32.066) and chlorine (35.457). In spite of the closeness in weight, they are poles apart chemically: sulfur is a yellow solid and chlorine a green gas, and the two behave very differently in chemical reactions.

On the other hand, just to make things more puzzling,

chemists found that some elements differing widely in atomic weight were very similar in their properties. For instance, sodium and potassium are very much alike, although the atomic weight of the second is nearly twice that of the first.

Was all the speculation about atomic weight barking up the wrong tree? Not quite. As early as 1817 one Johann Wolfgang Döbereiner, a German chemist, noticed something interesting.

Döbereiner was intrigued by the three elements calcium, barium, and strontium. All three are somewhat alike. What about their differences? Well, calcium melts at a temperature of 851 degrees centigrade, and barium melts at 710°C., while the melting point of strontium is in between: 800°C.

Then, take their chemical activity. Calcium is very active. A bit of calcium added to water will react with oxygen to liberate hydrogen. Barium is considerably more active; its reaction with water is far more vigorous. How about strontium? Its activity is in between.

All three elements form similar compounds: *e.g.*, calcium sulfate ($CaSO_4$), barium sulfate ($BaSO_4$), and strontium sulfate ($SrSO_4$). Now calcium sulfate is moderately soluble in water, barium sulfate hardly soluble at all, and—you've guessed it—strontium sulfate's solubility lies between theirs.

This in-betweeness of strontium shows up in a hundred other ways, too.

What interested Döbereiner most was how all this fitted in with the atomic-weight situation. According to Berzelius' measurements, the atomic weight of calcium was 40, that of barium was 137, and that of strontium was 88— almost exactly midway between!

In other words, strontium, which seemed to be halfway between calcium and barium in behavior, also was half-way between them in atomic weight.

Döbereiner dropped the matter there for a time. He was a man of many activities. Among other things, he became famous for inventing "Döbereiner's lamp," which was one of the first known devices to make use of a catalyst. In this device he fired a jet of hydrogen at some powdered platinum; on striking the platinum the hydrogen gas would burst into flame. Berzelius gave the name of "catalysis" to this process whereby a substance (such as platinum) brings about a reaction without being consumed itself.

Döbereiner also is known for another illustrious association: he became a close friend of Goethe and taught the great poet chemistry.

In 1829 Döbereiner returned to his numbers game with trios of elements. One of the new trios he looked at was sulfur, selenium, and tellurium. Here again was a triad of elements with very similar chemical properties, and one member—selenium—was halfway between the other two both in behavior and in atomic weight: sulfur's was 32, tellurium's 128, and selenium's 79. Döbereiner found a third case of the same thing. This one involved chlorine, bromine, and iodine. Chlorine is a light-colored, very active gas. Iodine is a very dark-colored and considerably less active solid. As for bromine? It is a middling-dark liquid with middling activity. It is middling in every other way, too. (In fact, when it was first discovered, some chemists thought it was a compound of chlorine and iodine.) And according to Berzelius' values, the atomic weight of chlorine was 35½, that of iodine was 127, and bromine stood squarely between at 80.

Döbereiner was fascinated. He took pains to report to the scientific world what he had observed about his "triads" of elements. But he was ahead of his time. The chemists of that day didn't get the point. They thought Döbereiner's game was just playing with numbers.

FINGERPRINTS IN COLOR

In the 1850's element-hunting suddenly took a new turn, thanks to the discovery of a new technique.

This harked back to Newton's old discovery that light had a spectrum of different colors. Newton separated the colors by passing sunlight through a glass prism. Later, chemists found that various substances emitted distinctive colors when they were heated. For instance, in 1758 the German chemist Marggraf (the man who first isolated zinc) noticed that soda burned with a yellow flame and potash turned a flame violet. In 1834 an English physicist, Henry Fox Talbot (who was one of the inventors of photography), carried this sort of color analysis a step farther. Lithium and strontium, it had been found, both burned with a red flame. Were their colors exactly the same, or was there some small difference between them? Talbot passed the light of each flame through a prism and found that the two spectra were indeed different.

Eventually a Pennsylvania physician named David Alter, after studying the light of many gases and metals, made the bold suggestion that each element had its own spectrum.

At this opportune moment two German physicists, Robert Wilhelm Bunsen and Gustav Robert Kirchoff, came forth with an invention (in 1859) which was just what the doctor would have ordered. Their invention was the spectroscope (a far more important invention than the one for which Bunsen is most famous—the Bunsen burner). Bunsen and Kirchoff devised a simple instrument which passed light through a narrow slit and then through a prism. The prism spread out the colors into a band extending the width of the rainbow spectrum. White light, containing all the colors, formed a continuous band. But when only certain colors were present in the light, these appeared as bright lines (images of the slit) at the appropriate places in the spectrum. Thus the flame of sodium, for instance, would show prominent lines in the yellow region of the spectrum (plus some secondary lines for less prominent colors in its flame).

Here at last was a quick, convenient means of identifying an element, or even a compound. Each element, Bunsen and Kirchoff found, had its own characteristic pattern of spectral lines—as distinctive as a fingerprint. Just heat a substance until it glowed, look at its line spectrum in the spectroscope, and you could tell at a glance what elements were present, even though some might be present only in very small quantities.

What's more, you could detect new elements whenever unfamiliar fingerprints showed up in your spectral analysis of a mineral or other sample of matter. Now unknown elements could be tracked down systematically, instead of hit-or-miss.

Bunsen and Kirchoff quickly found two new elements. Studying some samples of lithium-bearing minerals, they came across two strange lines, one blue and one red. The blue line turned out to belong to a new alkali metal which they named "cesium" (from the Latin for "blue"), and the red line belonged to a metal they called "rubidium" (from the Latin for "red").

THE SPECTROSCOPE IN EARTH AND SKY

The spectroscope was picked up by other chemists at once. The same year that rubidium was discovered, William Crookes of England found another new element in some salts formed in the manufacture of sulfuric acid. He was particularly interested in the element selenium, but when he heated these salts and studied the light by spectroscope, he discovered a new green line which drowned out the selenium lines. The green line revealed a new element which Crookes named "thallium," from a Greek word meaning "green twig."

Then a color-blind German physicist named Ferdinand Reich, teamed up with a chemist named Hieronymus Theodor Richter, added another to the list in 1863. They were studying a zinc mineral with the spectroscope. Richter, who was not color-blind, noticed an indigo-colored line which matched no known lines. They named this element "indium."

Meanwhile the spectroscope was also being taken up by astronomers to examine the stars. Many years before the instrument was invented, the German physicist Joseph von Fraunhofer had used a prism to analyze sunlight passed through a slit. He found hundreds of dark lines (still called "Fraunhofer lines") in the sun's spectrum. The dark lines were a mystery until the invention of the spectroscope made possible laboratory experiments which explained them.

The spectroscope showed that elements in a cool (*i.e.,* non-glowing) state would *absorb* light at the same wavelengths they emitted when they glowed. For instance, hot hydrogen gas shows bright lines at certain blue wavelengths; cold hydrogen will absorb light at just those wavelengths. Therefore when the spectroscope receives light which has passed through cold hydrogen, dark lines will appear in the spectrum at those wavelengths.

What, then, did the Fraunhofer lines in the spectrum of the sun's light mean? They must mean that cool gases in the sun's atmosphere absorbed some of the light coming out of the sun. If that was so, then the dark lines were the fingerprints of elements in the sun's atmosphere. In other words, the spectroscope now made it possible for man to find out what elements were present in the atmospheres of heavenly bodies—not only the sun but also other stars and even the planets.

Astronomers quickly found out that the elements in the heavenly bodies were the same as the elements of the earth. Old Aristotle had been quite wrong: the celestial universe was not made of some special "aether" or "quintessence" but of just the same stuff as our own planet.

True, one element unknown on the earth did turn up in the sun. In 1868 astronomers looked at the sun's atmosphere with a spectroscope during a solar eclipse, and Pierre Jules César Janssen of France noticed a new yellow line. An English astronomer, Norman Lockyer, suggested that this represented a new element; he called it "helium" (from the Greek word for the sun). Chemists didn't accept this at the time. Helium was not added officially to the list of elements until many years later, when it was found on the earth.

Table 11 lists the four elements that were discovered

Table 11

ELEMENTS DISCOVERED WITH THE NEW SPECTROSCOPE				
ELEMENT	SYMBOL	ATOMIC WEIGHT	YEAR DISCOVERED	DISCOVERER
Cesium	Cs	132.91	1860	Bunsen Kirchhoff
Rubidium	Rb	85.48	1861	Bunsen Kirchhoff
Thallium	Tl	204.39	1861	Crookes
Indium	In	114.82	1863	Reich Richter

with the spectroscope shortly after the invention of the instrument.

The list of elements had now grown to 62. It was still
just a list. With the exception of Döbereiner, no one had
seen any kind of rhyme or reason in the collection. It was
high time that someone sat down and tried to arrange or
classify the elements in some sort of order.

11

IN ORDER OF ATOMIC WEIGHT

There are various logical ways in which one might list the elements: in the chronological order of their discovery (as I have done in most of the tables thus far), or alphabetically, or in the order of atomic weight. This last arrangement (see Table 12) at least makes some physical sense. But it holds few charms from the standpoint of clarifying anything about the elements' properties.

In 1862 a French geologist named Alexandre Emile Béguyer de Chancourtois amused himself by writing down the list of elements in a spiraling column, like a stripe on a barber pole. The interesting thing about this playful arrangement was that Döbereiner's triads fell into line in a related order. For instance, the triad of calcium, strontium, and barium were in one vertical line, with strontium just under calcium and barium under strontium. The same was true of the triad chlorine, bromine, and iodine, and also the triad sulfur, selenium, and tellurium.

Béguyer de Chancourtois called his arrangement the "telluric screw." He published a paper on it, but everyone missed the point. In the first place, he was a poor writer; in

Table 12

THE ELEMENTS OF 1863 IN ORDER OF ATOMIC WEIGHT

ELEMENT	ATOMIC WEIGHT	ELEMENT	ATOMIC WEIGHT
Hydrogen	1.0080	Zirconium	91.22
Lithium	6.940	Niobium	92.91
Beryllium	9.013	Molybdenum	95.95
Boron	10.82	Ruthenium	101.1
Carbon	12.011	Rhodium	102.91
Nitrogen	14.008	Palladium	106.4
Oxygen	16.0000	Silver	107.88
Sodium	22.991	Cadmium	112.41
Magnesium	24.32	Indium	114.82
Aluminum	26.98	Tin	118.70
Silicon	28.09	Antimony	121.76
Phosphorus	30.975	Iodine	126.91
Sulfur	32.066	Tellurium	127.61
Chlorine	35.457	Cesium	132.91
Potassium	39.100	Barium	137.36
Calcium	40.08	Lanthanum	138.92
Titanium	47.90	Cerium	140.13
Vanadium	50.95	Terbium	158.93
Chromium	52.01	Erbium	167.27
Manganese	54.94	Tantalum	180.95
Iron	55.85	Tungsten	183.86
Nickel	58.71	Osmium	190.2
Cobalt	58.94	Iridium	192.2
Copper	63.54	Platinum	195.09
Zinc	65.38	Gold	197.0
Arsenic	74.91	Mercury	200.61
Selenium	78.96	Thallium	204.39
Bromine	79.916	Lead	207.21
Rubidium	85.48	Bismuth	209.00
Strontium	87.63	Thorium	232.05
Yttrium	88.92	Uranium	238.07

the second, he used geological terminology, so chemists didn't understand him; and in the third place, the publication neglected to include his diagram showing the elements arranged on the cylinder. His paper didn't make so much as a ripple in the chemical world.

But a good idea is bound to come up again sooner or later. In 1864 an English chemist named John Alexander Reina Newlands also played around with listing the elements in columns. He found that, by dividing the list into columns of seven elements each (in the order of atomic weight), he got a definite pattern of family resemblances. His first three columns are shown in Table 13.

Table 13

PART OF NEWLANDS' ARRANGEMENT OF THE ELEMENTS

FIRST COLUMN	SECOND COLUMN	THIRD COLUMN
Hydrogen	Fluorine	Chlorine
Lithium	Sodium	Potassium
Beryllium	Magnesium	Calcium
Boron	Aluminum	Chromium
Carbon	Silicon	Titanium
Nitrogen	Phosphorus	Manganese
Oxygen	Sulfur	Iron

(Newlands included fluorine because its existence was already suspected, though it was not yet on the official list. He should have put vanadium in the third column—after titanium—but he had the wrong atomic weight for that element and so placed it much farther down the list.)

THE LAW OF OCTAVES

Now let's look at Newlands' first column and see what we can make of it.

First comes hydrogen, a fairly active gas. Next, lithium, an active solid. Then beryllium, a less active solid; then boron, a still less active solid; then carbon, an even less active solid. After that, nitrogen, an inactive gas; finally, oxygen, an active gas.

So far, this doesn't seem to mean much. Let's try the second column.

First there's fluorine, an active gas; then sodium, an active solid; magnesium, a less active solid; aluminum, a still less active solid; and silicon, an even less active solid.

Now we are getting somewhere. The second column is repeating the pattern of the first. Furthermore, the resemblances are not just superficial. Fluorine has several chemical similarities to hydrogen, and sodium is very similar indeed to lithium. Likewise, magnesium, aluminum, and silicon are chemically like beryllium, boron, and carbon, respectively.

The last two elements in the second column, phosphorus and sulfur, are a little disappointing. They are not gases, like their counterparts, nitrogen and oxygen, in the first column. And yet there are chemical similarities. Phosphorus combines with other elements in much the same way as nitrogen, and the same goes for sulfur and oxygen.

What about the third column? First comes chlorine, an active gas very much like fluorine. Potassium, second in the column, is an active solid and a chemical cousin of sodium and lithium, number 2 in the first and second columns, respectively. Calcium, number 3 in the third column, resembles beryllium and magnesium in the first two columns. And so on.

Newlands was sure he had something. His table beautifully explained Döbereiner's triads. Chlorine headed the third column; bromine headed the fifth; and iodine headed the seventh column. To this triad Newlands now could add hydrogen and fluorine, which led the first and second columns and bore chemical similarities to chlorine, bromine, and iodine.

Again, Döbereiner's triad of calcium, strontium, and barium were all in the third place in their respective columns, and to these, beryllium and magnesium could be added. Finally, sulfur, selenium, and tellurium, the third triad, were all at the bottom of the columns.

Döbereiner had been on the right track; he had simply not gone far enough. Newlands' table now revealed not triads but quintets and even larger families of similar elements. All you had to do to find families was to read horizontally across the columns.

Newlands was reminded of the octaves of the musical scale. Just as music had its octaves, so his table of elements had octave intervals, with seven elements in each group (corresponding to the seven notes do, re, mi, fa, sol, la, ti). Newlands named his discovery the "law of octaves."

Unfortunately, Newlands' table had some bad flaws. Some of the elements obviously didn't fit into the places he had assigned to them. For instance iron, the last element in the third column, was completely different in every way from oxygen and sulfur, the last-place members of the first and second columns; it didn't even form the same kind of compounds. Then, consider the elements at the top of Newlands' eight columns:

Hydrogen, fluorine, chlorine, bromine, and iodine certainly could all be placed in the same family. But cobalt, nickel, palladium, platinum, and iridium just did not belong with these. You couldn't imagine two elements less alike than fluorine and iridium. Fluorine is the most active element in the whole list and iridium is the least active. Fluorine is a gas and iridium is a metal.

Furthermore, to maintain the rhythm of likenesses in his octaves, Newlands had to double up elements in some

first column	hydrogen
second column	fluorine
third column	chlorine
fourth column	cobalt and nickel
fifth column	bromine
sixth column	palladium
seventh column	iodine
eighth column	platinum and iridium

positions: *e.g.*, cobalt with nickel and platinum with iridium. He also had to place some elements in the wrong order of atomic weight. For instance, he put chromium ahead of titanium, although he knew that its atomic weight was greater, because chromium seemed more like aluminum than like silicon (see Table 13).

Most chemists ridiculed Newlands' table, and scientific journals refused to publish his article describing the law of octaves.

The fact is that Newlands basically had the right idea but had made a simple mistake which threw his table hopelessly askew. The flaw lay in his "law of octaves": he had gone wrong in counting off by sevens for all his columns.

LENGTHENING THE PERIODS

In 1870, six years after Newlands' brilliant but abortive inspiration, a German chemist named Julius Lothar Meyer put his finger on the trouble. Meyer took the opposite approach to arraying the elements: instead of trying to fit them into a hard-and-fast arrangement, as Béguyer de Chancourtois and Newlands had done, he let the properties of the elements dictate the arrangement.

Meyer concentrated on one particular property—

weight. He wondered about the odd fact that the bulk weights of the elements (the weight of a given volume of the substance when you put it on a scale) were not consistent with their relative atomic weights. Take, for instance, cesium and barium. In bulk, barium is nearly twice as heavy as cesium: barium's specific gravity (its weight compared to that of an equal volume of water) is 3.78, while cesium's is only 1.903. Yet both have close to the same atomic weight: 132.91 for cesium and 137.36 for barium.

That could only mean one thing: in their bulk agglomerations barium atoms must be packed together twice as closely as cesium atoms. To put it another way, the "atomic volume" of barium was only half that of cesium.

Meyer went through the whole list of elements, plotting atomic volume against atomic weight, and he got a graph which took the form of a series of waves.

To show the result as simply as possible, I have drawn a simplified form of his graph, leaving out hydrogen and starting with lithium, the second lightest element then known (see Table 14). Lithium has a certain atomic volume. Meyer found that the atomic volumes of the elements following it declined at first (*i.e.*, for beryllium and boron) and then began to rise (*i.e.*, carbon, nitrogen, oxygen, fluorine, and sodium had successively larger atomic volumes). Sodium reached a peak (higher that lithium); after that, the atomic volumes began to fall again, and then rise until they reached a higher peak at potassium. And so it went down the list of elements, the atomic volumes rising and falling like a set of waves.

Now notice that the peaks in the partial diagram here are lithium, sodium, potassium, rubidium, and cesium. These are all alkali metals. They form a true, consistent pattern of closely related elements. It turns out that the same thing holds true of the series of elements at the bottoms of the waves and of those in other positions on the waves. In other words, when Meyer classified the elements according to atomic volume in relation to atomic weight, they fell into families.

Table 14

A SIMPLE DIAGRAM OF MEYER'S ATOMIC VOLUMES

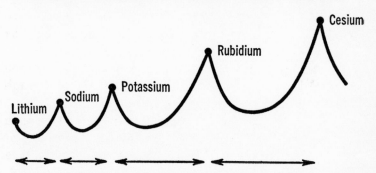

The diagram brings out a significant fact which shows where Newlands went wrong. The waves get longer as we go down the list of elements (or "up" the list, considering their increasing atomic weight). The first two waves (lithium to sodium and sodium to potassium) are about the same length; the next two are more than twice as long. If Newlands had made his later columns twice as long as his first two (combining columns 3 and 4, 5 and 6, and 7 and 8), he would have solved some of his difficulties. The five columns then would have been headed by hydrogen, fluorine, chlorine, bromine, and iodine—all clearly related chemicals. Cobalt, nickel, palladium, platinum, and iridium would not have come into the picture to foul things up.

Meyer, as I have mentioned, published his graph in 1870. History might have made him a very famous man. But he was just one year too late. In 1869 a Russian chemist had published a table which was to become the enduring bible of the elements.

12

THE PERIODIC TABLE

That this great contribution to chemistry came from Russia was quite startling in itself. In the eighteenth and nineteenth centuries chemistry was almost a monopoly of the western countries of Europe, particularly Germany, Sweden, France, and England. Russia was far behind in science and all other forms of learning. Its people were deliberately kept illiterate by the despotic Russian tsars, who feared that education of the peasants would lead to revolution.

Even so, in the eighteenth century Russia had produced one of the most brilliant chemists of all time—Mikhail Vassilievich Lomonosov (1711-1765). The son of a poor fisherman in a far northern village, he somehow managed to get to Moscow to educate himself. He showed such promise in school there that he was sent to Germany for an education in chemistry.

Lomonosov distinguished himself in many fields; he wrote some of the best poetry in the Russian language; he reformed the language by simplifying its grammar; and he became the Lavoisier of Russia. He is today one of the most revered figures in Russian history. Among other honors, the name Lomonosov has been given to the village in which he was born and also to one of the craters on the far side of the moon, which a Soviet sputnik photographed for the first time in 1959.

But in his own time Lomonosov was scarcely known at all outside Russia. Scientists in other countries did not read Russian reports; indeed most of them didn't even know the language. (They still don't today, though many of them wish they did.) Had the eighteenth-century chemists read Lomonosov's writings, they would have learned that he solved the problem of the chemistry of combustion (by performing experiments like Lavoisier's) 20 years before Lavoisier did!

After Lavoisier had published his theory of combustion (independently of Lomonosov), it was another Russian chemist, Vassily Vladimirovich Petrov, who worked out conclusive experiments that proved it. In 1797 he showed that in a vacuum (*i.e.,* without oxygen) phosphorus would not burn and metals did not form calxes. This was a particularly convincing disproof of the phlogiston theory and demonstration of the importance of oxygen. But western chemists did not hear about Petrov's work, either.

The Russian we are concerned with here, however, was not Lomonosov or Petrov but one Dmitri Ivanovich Mendeléev.

Mendeléev was born in Siberia in the city of Tobolsk. His mother is supposed to have been part Mongol. Dmitri was the youngest of some 14 or 17 children (the records are not clear about the exact number). His father was the principal of the local high school, but he went blind when Dmitri was very young. To support the large family, Dmitri's mother started a glass factory.

When Dmitri was 16 and finishing high school, his

father died and his mother's factory burned down. The incredibly energetic and determined woman decided that her youngest and brightest boy must be given a higher education, come what might. She set off with Dmitri for Moscow, thousands of miles away. There she was rebuffed: the university would not admit Dmitri. Gritting her teeth, she went on to St. Petersburg. There a friend of her dead husband finally was able to get the youngster into college. Her mission accomplished, Mrs. Mendeléev died soon afterward.

Dmitri Mendeléev was bent for science, to which he had been drawn by his first teacher, a political exile in Siberia. He finished college at the top of his class. Then he went to France and Germany for the training he could not get in Russia.

In Germany he worked with Bunsen, who had just invented the spectroscope. Mendeléev also attended the Congress at Karlsruhe and must have been profoundly influenced by Cannizzaro's great speech on atomic weights.

The young Siberian returned to St. Petersburg and at the age of 32 became a full professor of chemistry. He soon established himself as the most interesting lecturer in Russia, and one of the best in all Europe. He also wrote a chemistry textbook, called *The Principles of Chemistry,* which was probably the best ever written in Russian.

VALENCE AND THE TABLE

In the late 1860's Mendeléev, like so many chemists before him, tackled the problem of finding some sort of order in the list of elements. Meyer in Germany was working on the problem from the point of view of atomic volumes. Mendeléev, unaware of Meyer's work, approached the matter from a different angle. His starting point was the "valences" of the elements.

For many years it had been known that each element

had a certain "combining power." The hydrogen atom, for instance, could not take on more than one other atom at a time: it never combined with two atoms of oxygen, say, to form HO_2. Oxygen, on the other hand, could combine with two, but only two, other atoms (*e.g.*, H_2O). We might say that the hydrogen atom is monogamous and the oxygen atom is bigamous.

Hydrogen, then, has a "combining power" of one. So have sodium, fluorine, bromine, potassium, iodine, and a few other elements. Oxygen and a number of other elements have a combining power of two. Nitrogen and others have a combining power of three (*e.g.*, NH_3). And so on.

In 1852 an English chemist named Edward Frankland coined the term "valence" (from a Latin word meaning "power") to denote combining power. Each element was assigned a valence, according to its chemical behavior.

Now Mendeléev concentrated on the valences of the elements. Did they show any kind of pattern? He listed the elements in order of molecular weight and wrote down the valence beside each element. Table 15 shows part of the list.

As you see, the value of the valence moves up and down evenly. Starting at 1, it goes up to 4 and back down to 1, then up to 4 and back down to 1 again. Later in the list, matters aren't quite so even and simple, but valence continues to move up and down in waves. The waves become longer, however (just as Meyer was discovering in his graph of atomic volumes).

On the basis of the cycles, or "periods," revealed by the valences, Mendeléev composed a "periodic table" of the elements. This time all Europe took notice of a Russian's work. Mendeléev's 1869 paper was promptly translated into German and published for chemists everywhere.

Mendeléev kept working on his table and improving

it. After Meyer's graph was published in 1870, Mendeléev found that it clarified some points which valence had left hazy. By the time Mendeléev was through, his table looked pretty much like the one chemists still use today.

Table 15

VALENCES OF ELEMENTS IN ORDER OF ATOMIC WEIGHT

ELEMENT	VALENCE
Hydrogen	1
Lithium	1
Beryllium	2
Boron	3
Carbon	4
Nitrogen	3
Oxygen	2
Fluorine	1
Sodium	1
Magnesium	2
Aluminum	3
Silicon	4
Phosphorus	3
Sulfur	2
Chlorine	1
Potassium	1
Calcium	2

In Table 16 I present the elements then known in an arrangement close to the one Mendeléev finally reached. I have made a few changes to bring it more in line with our current ideas on the subject, and I have also included the modern values of the atomic weights.

This table has seven columns, usually named "first period," "second period," and so on. In the first period

Table 16

THE Periodic Table AS IT LOOKED IN 1869

	First Period	Second Period	Third Period
row Ia	Hydrogen (1.0080)	Lithium (6.940)	Sodium (22.991)
row IIa		Beryllium (9.013)	Magnesium (24.32)
row IIIa			
row IVa			
row Va			
row VIa			
row VIIa			
row VIII			
row Ib			
row IIb			
row IIIb		Boron (10.82)	Aluminum (26.98)
row IVb		Carbon (12.011)	Silicon (28.09)
row Vb		Nitrogen (14.008)	Phosphorus (30.975)
row VIb		Oxygen (16.0000)	Sulfur (32.006)
row VIIb		Fluorine (19.00)	Chlorine (35.457)

Table 16 (cont.)

Fourth Period	Fifth Period	Sixth Period	Seventh Period
Potassium (39.100)	Rubidium (85.48)	Cesium (132.91)	
Calcium (40.08)	Strontium (87.63)	Barium (137.36)	
	Yttrium (88.92)	Lanthanum (138.92)	
Titanium (47.90)	Zirconium (91.22)		Thorium (232.05)
Vanadium (50.95)	Niobium (92.91)	Tantalum (180.95)	
Chromium (52.01)	Molybdenum (95.95)	Tungsten (183.86)	Uranium (238.07)
Manganese (54.94)			
Iron (55.85)	Ruthenium (101.1)	Osmium (190.2)	
Cobalt (58.94)	Rhodium (102.91)	Iridium (192.2)	
Nickel (58.71)	Palladium (106.4)	Platinum (195.09)	
Copper (63.54)	Silver (107.88)	Gold (197.0)	
Zinc (65.38)	Cadmium (112.41)	Mercury (200.61)	
	Indium (114.82)	Thallium (204.39)	
	Tin (118.70)	Lead (207.21)	
Arsenic (74.91)	Antimony (121.76)	Bismuth (209.00)	
Selenium (78.96)	Tellurium (127.61)		
Bromine (79.916)	Iodine (126.91)		

there is only one element, hydrogen. The second and third periods have seven elements apiece, as in Newlands' table. The fourth, fifth, and sixth periods, however, are considerably longer. In order to line up similar elements horizontally, a gap has to be left in the middle section of the short periods. By convention, the rows are all labelled with Roman numerals according to a system that depends on valence.

First of all, we can note that Döbereiner's triads fall into place. Chlorine, bromine, and iodine are in the same row; so are sulfur, selenium, and tellurium, and also calcium, strontium, and barium.

What's more, any chemist will recognize that all the elements in a row can be considered to belong to the same family. For instance, lithium, sodium, potassium, rubidium, and cesium are definitely alike chemically; copper, silver, and gold are metals with many properties in common; likewise, carbon, silicon, tin, and lead share chemical similarities.

In row VIII there are sets of three elements called "triads" (though they are not Döbereiner's triads). The members of each triad are alike, and the triads in turn resemble one another; indeed, the two triads ruthenium-rhodium-palladium and osmium-iridium-platinum are all called platinum metals.

Not only are the elements in a row related, but there are also similarities between rows, as is indicated by the labels Ia and Ib, IIa and IIIb, and so on. Hydrogen is a particularly dramatic example of the kinship between rows: it could be placed in row VIIb as well as in Ia, as far as its similarity to the other members of the row is concerned.

For the first time, Mendeléev's table made some sense out of the mob of elements. It organized them into clear-cut families. It was not a piecemeal picture of coincidences, as

Döbereiner's triads were; nor did it mix up bad matches with good ones, as Newland's table had. Mendeléev presented all the families in such a logical arrangement that it was impossible to consider it coincidence.

The world of chemistry couldn't help being impressed. Yet chemists could not bring themselves to accept the table at face value. It was too pat—too good to be true. They wanted proof.

What put the cap on Mendeléev's remarkable achievement, and his fame, was the startling way in which that proof was found.

THE HOLES IN THE TABLE

Mendeléev was so confident of the validity of his periodic table that he didn't hesitate to contradict established ideas about individual elements and to make very risky predictions.

Like Newlands, he placed tellurium ahead of iodine in his table in spite of its higher atomic weight, because the switch put these elements in the proper rows with their chemical cousins. But Mendeléev did not juggle the elements in wholesale fashion, as Newlands had done, and he was eventually proved right in making this exception.*

Mendeléev made some other shifts which shocked chemists even more. Beryllium was supposed to have an atomic weight of about 14. Impossible, said Mendeléev; there was no vacancy for an element of that weight in his table. He put beryllium in row IIa alongside magnesium, which it resembled. This meant that beryllium must fall

---

* If you look at Table 16, you will see that cobalt and nickel are in the wrong order, too. However, these elements are so similar in behavior and atomic weight that it's a tossup which to put first and which second. Mendeléev's guess that cobalt was first and nickel second turned out to be right.

between lithium and boron in atomic weight; that is, its atomic weight should be about 9. Sure enough, it was eventually established to be 9.013. Similarly, he said that the chemists were wrong in their atomic weights for indium and uranium, too, and the weights he gave these two elements were later proved correct.

But Mendeléev's most daring climb out on a limb was an assertion about certain missing elements. To make his periodic table work, he had to leave several holes in it.

Here, for example, was a gap between zinc (atomic weight: 65.38) and arsenic (atomic weight: 74.91). Zinc belonged in row IIb because it was very much like cadmium, and arsenic should be in row Vb because it was like antimony (see Table 16). But what about the places in rows IIIb and IVb which were left vacant? There were no known elements with atomic weights between those of zinc and arsenic.

Indeed! said Mendeléev. Well, then, we must look for them. Said Mendeléev: there are two elements missing here which without question exist on earth and will be found.

He proceeded to describe the truant elements. One, he said, would have properties intermediate between those of aluminum and indium, for it belonged between them in row IIIb. He predicted that this element, which he called "eka-aluminum," would have an atomic weight of about 68, a specific gravity of about 5.9, and a low melting point. It should be unaffected by air and should react slowly with acids. It would form an oxide composed of eka-aluminum atoms and three oxygen atoms in the molecule. Mendeléev went on to describe the behavior of the oxide and some other compounds of eka-aluminum.

The second unknown element, he predicted, would have properties between those of silicon and tin (in row IVb). This one he called "eka-silicon." Its atomic weight would be 72, and its specific gravity 5.5. It would combine with two atoms of oxygen to form a dioxide and four atoms of chlorine to form a tetrachloride. The tetrachloride, he said, would boil at a temperature below 100° C.

Mendeléev's table had a third vacancy in the fourth period—this one next to yttrium in row IIIa (see Table 16). Mendeléev was sure that an element was missing there also, and that its properties should be like those of yttrium and lanthanum. It should also have some kinship to elements in row IIIb, because that family is related to IIIa. The row IIIb elements in the second and third periods are boron and aluminum. Mendeléev had already named one of his missing elements eka-aluminum, so he called this third one "eka-boron."

Eka-boron, he predicted, would have an atomic weight of 44 and would form an oxide similar to aluminum oxide. Its compounds would be colorless and would have certain other specified properties.

A more specific, and riskier, challenge could hardly have been conceived. If such elements were actually found, Mendeléev would be a hero and his periodic table verified beyond cavil. If they did not exist, Mendeléev would turn out to be one of the most ludicrous crystal-ball gazers in the history of chemistry.

13

THE MISSING
ELEMENTS

At first chemists refused to take Mendeléev's predictions seriously. Many foolish things had been done in the name of chemistry, but no one had ever attempted to conjure up elements out of pure imagination. People had deduced elements from the death of mice, from the colors of minerals, from mere lines in a spectrum. But Mendeléev had nothing—only a table he had written down which happened to have some empty spaces. Yet he presumed to describe, down to the smallest details, elements which had never given any tangible sign of their existence.

Mendeléev paid no attention to the snickers and waited for developments. As it happened, he didn't have to wait long.

A young French chemist named Paul Émile Lecoq de Boisbaudran, working in a small laboratory of his own, became so fascinated by the spectroscope that year after year he pored over minerals with his instrument. One day in 1874 he detected some strange spectral lines in a mineral that had come from zinc mines in the Pyrenees. A new element? In high excitement he hurried to Paris to show important chemists what he had found. Then he went to work to isolate the element.

From hundreds of pounds of mineral he finally got a few tiny scraps of an odd metal. It melted at the low temperature of 30° C.: it would slowly melt even in the warmth of a person's hand. Lecoq de Boisbaudran named the element "gallium," from the old Latin name for France. (Some believe that he also named it for himself, since Lecoq means "rooster" and *gallus* is the Latin word for rooster.)

The French chemist was elated by his discovery, but he could not have been half as excited as Mendeléev. As soon as the Russian read the description of the new element, he knew it was his eka-aluminum. He had predicted that the element would have a low melting point. He had estimated its atomic weight to be about 68, and gallium's was 69.72. He had predicted its specific gravity would be 5.9; gallium's was 5.94. Its chemical behavior followed his predictions. Point by point, gallium matched eka-aluminum in every way.

The remarkable match caused a sensation. Chemists had to admit that gallium was Mendeléev's eka-aluminum all right. His periodic table, it now appeared, was not just an ingenious doodle on paper. It might indeed be a key to systematic interpretation of the elements and of chemistry itself.

It was perhaps the most exciting moment in all the long history of the search for the elements. At last someone had learned enough about the elements to predict the existence of one that had never been suspected.

Four years later the second of Mendeléev's predictions was fulfilled. Lars Fredrick Nilson, a Swedish chemist, was studying a newly discovered mineral. Quite accidentally he came upon an unfamiliar oxide. He decided it was the oxide of a new element, and he named it "scandium," in honor of Scandinavia, where the mineral was found.

It was another Swedish element hunter, Per Teodor Cleve, who noticed that scandium resembled one of Mendeléev's missing elements. It behaved just as Mendeléev had predicted eka-boron would behave. Again Mendeléev's description of the element turned out to be almost exactly correct in every detail. The atomic weight of scandium was 44.96 (the prediction: 44); scandium oxide had a specific gravity of 3.86 (prediction: 3.5); and so on.

Mendeléev's final triumph came in 1886. A German chemist, Clemens Alexander Winkler, was analyzing a mineral from a silver mine and was having trouble. After breaking it down to all the elements he could identify, he wound up with 7 per cent of the mineral left over. Winkler decided that this must represent an unknown element. He worked on it for months and finally succeeded in extracting the element. He named it "germanium" for Germany.*

By now chemists were on the lookout for Mendeléev's third element. Germanium, Winkler quickly found out, was indeed that third one—eka-silicon. Its atomic weight was 72.60 (almost exactly the predicted 72); its specific gravity was 5.47 (prediction: 5.5). Just as Mendeléev had said, the element formed a tetrachloride with a low boiling point. Mendeléev was wrong on only one count; germanium melted at a lower temperature than he had forecast.

Mendeléev had come up to bat three times and hit three home runs. His periodic table was now recognized as a momentous discovery.

The rulers of Russia hastened to heap honors on their great scientist. They sent him on a mission to the United States (another country much underrated at the time by

---

* It is an odd coincidence that all three elements predicted by Mendeléev were named after the native lands of the discoverers.

western Europeans) to study the oilfields of Pennsylvania
for guidance in developing the oilfields of the Caucasus.

Meanwhile the most aristocratic scientific societies of
Europe also embraced Mendeléev. The Royal Society of
London awarded him the coveted Davy Medal in 1882.
Other medals and awards followed.

Mendeléev was a bold pioneer in other fields besides
chemistry. In 1887 he went up in a balloon to photograph
a solar eclipse. There is a picture of him standing erect in
the gondola with great dignity, looking like a Biblical
patriarch in his flowing locks and long beard. Mendeléev
also spoke up bravely against the Tsarist government in
defense of rebellious students. Like many other Russian
intellectuals, he was shocked and dismayed by Russia's de-
feat by Japan in the war of 1904, but he did not live to see
the inevitable revolution against the Tsarist regime.

The triumph of Mendeléev's periodic table also
brought recognition and vindication to Meyer, to Newlands,
and even to Béguyer de Chancourtois. In fact, in 1891 a
French scientific journal belatedly printed the diagram of
the latter's "telluric screw."

THE UNPREDICTED ELEMENTS

Now came the task of filling out the table. Mendeléev's
scheme suggested that there was a limited number of elements. All the chemist had to do now was to complete his
rows and periods and to verify the existence of those elements that had not yet been isolated. So, at least, it seemed.

Fluorine was one element that had stubbornly resisted
isolation. The chemists knew where they could find it, but
they had had no luck in separating it from its compounds.
In 1886, by heroic efforts, a French chemist named Henri
Moissan finally trapped it.

Fluorine had defied liberation because it was extremely

active. It attacked water, most metals, and even glass, so that laboratory equipment soaked it up as fast as it was liberated. Furthermore, it also attacked living tissue, and Moissan was badly poisoned several times in his experiments.

He finally hit upon a winning strategy. For containers to hold the gas he used an alloy of platinum and iridium, the most inert metals known. To slow up fluorine's activity, he cooled his equipment to as low a temperature as he could obtain. By these tactics he managed at last to trap some free fluorine within his vessels of noble metal. In 1906, the year before his death, he received the Nobel prize in chemistry for this achievement.

(Moissan won another kind of fame by announcing that he had made artificial diamonds from carbon by dissolving it in molten iron. He showed some diamond chips to support his claim. But it is now known that his method could not have worked. One theory is that an assistant slipped some diamond chips into the professor's preparation as a practical joke.)

After the discovery of gallium, scandium, and germanium, there were three holes left in Mendeléev's table—one in the fifth period and two in the sixth. Nobody doubted that these would eventually be filled by new discoveries. But a bothersome detail had everybody puzzled. There were several known elements for which no room could be found in the table!

The trouble started with three rare-earth elements—cerium, erbium, and terbium. Mendeléev's table had no proper place for them, and he had to squeeze them in awkwardly. (I left these elements out of Table 16 to avoid confusion.)

Those flyspecks on an otherwise perfect picture might have been overlooked, but as time went on, more embarrassments appeared. The list of new elements that couldn't be fitted into the table kept growing!

In 1879 Lecoq de Boisbaudran, still at his spectroscope, came across some new spectral lines in a Russian rare-earth mineral called samarskite. He traced these to a new element which he named "samarium." Meanwhile Cleve (the chemist who recognized scandium as Mendeléev's eka-boron) spotted two other rare-earth elements with the spectroscope. He named one "holmium," for Stockholm, and the second "thulium," for Thule, the old Latin name for the lands of the far North. For the discovery of holmium, a French physicist named Louis Soret shares the credit with Cleve, because he noted its spectral lines at about the same time.

The rare-earth elements kept multiplying like weeds. Lecoq de Boisbaudran found, in the same ore with holmium, another element which he named "dysprosium," from a Greek word meaning "hard to get at." A Swiss chemist, Jean-Charles Galissard de Marignac, picked up a new element he called "ytterbium"—the fourth to be named for the hamlet of Ytterby. He went on to discover still another in the holmium ore; Lecoq de Boisbaudran, who also found it, suggested that it be named "gadolinium," in honor of Johan Gadolin, the discoverer of the first rare-earth element. And an Austrian chemist, Carl Auer von Welsbach, turned up two nearly identical elements which he named "praseodymium" ("green twin") and "neodymium" ("new twin").

Here, then, were eight more elements that had to be added to the periodic table. Where did they fit in? Nowhere, as far as anybody could see. Along with cerium, erbium, and terbium, they made a total of eleven homeless elements for which there were no appropriate vacancies.

Logically all eleven belonged in row IIIa, along with the other known rare-earth elements. All the rare-earth elements were very much alike; all had a valence of 3; and all seemed to go together. But the boxes in row IIIa were already filled by scandium, yttrium, and lanthanum (see Table 16). And the eleven homeless elements came right after lanthanum in atomic weight, as Table 17 shows. This meant they had to be put in the sixth period. The only place they could go in that period, according to their chemical properties, was in the same box with the rare-earth lanthanum. In short, to make the table work, 12 elements had to be crammed into that one box. Mendeléev's neat table was turning out to be not so neat after all.

Table 17

RARE-EARTH ELEMENTS KNOWN IN 1886

ELEMENT	ATOMIC WEIGHT
Scandium	44.96
Yttrium	88.92
Lanthanum	138.92
Cerium	140.13
Praseodymium	140.92
Neodymium	144.27
Samarium	150.35
Gadolinium	157.26
Terbium	158.93
Dysprosium	162.51
Holmium	164.94
Erbium	167.27
Thulium	168.94
Ytterbium	173.04

More complications were to come, as I shall relate presently.

To bring our chronicle of element-discoveries up to date, I list in Table 18 the elements discovered in the years following the publication of Mendeléev's table. The list of elements had now grown to 74.

Table 18

ELEMENTS DISCOVERED IN THE TIME OF MENDELÉEV

Element	Symbol	Atomic Weight	Year Discovered	Discoverer
Gallium	Ga	69.72	1875	Boisbaudran
Holmium	Ho	164.94	1878	{ Cleve { Soret
Ytterbium	Yb	173.04	1878	Marignac
Samarium	Sm	150.35	1879	Boisbaudran
Thulium	Tm	168.94	1879	Cleve
Scandium	Sc	44.96	1879	Nilson
Gadolinium	Gd	157.26	1880	Marignac
Praseodymium	Pr	140.92	1885	Welsbach
Neodymium	Nd	144.27	1885	Welsbach
Germanium	Ge	72.60	1886	Winkler
Dysprosium	Dy	162.51	1886	Boisbaudran
Fluorine	F	19.00	1886	Moissan

THE UNPREDICTED ROW

At the end of the nineteenth century another stunning surprise upset the chemists. There came to light a new series of elements that found no home in Mendeléev's table. But this time the solution was easy. Mendeléev had simply left out a whole row!

The story really begins with a puzzling fact that Henry Cavendish had discovered a century earlier. He had tried to find out whether there were any gases in air besides oxygen and nitrogen. Removing oxygen from his sample of air was no problem; he got rid of it easily. Nitrogen was a tougher affair, because it refused to form compounds to be removed. But Cavendish finally managed to force it into combination with some very active chemicals. In the end he was left with about 1 per cent of the original air which wouldn't combine with anything. He decided that this remaining gas could not be nitrogen. It must be even more inert than nitrogen. But there was no way to identify the gas, and other chemists ignored Cavendish's conjecture that it was a new element.

In the 1890's Robert John Strutt, the famous physicist better known as Lord Rayleigh, revived the question. He found that the "nitrogen" from air weighed slightly more than samples of nitrogen from nitrogen-containing minerals. Did this perhaps mean that some unknown, heavier gas was mixed with the nitrogen he had obtained from air? Lord Rayleigh put an assistant, a Scottish chemist named William Ramsay, to work on the problem.

Ramsay repeated Cavendish's experiment and likewise came down finally to a bubble of completely inert gas.

But now he had the spectroscope, as Cavendish had not had, to examine this gas. He heated it to a glow, and its spectrum showed new lines. It was a new element, all right. Ramsay called it "argon," from a Greek word meaning "inert."

Where could argon be placed in the periodic table? Its atomic weight, 39.944, lay between those of potassium and calcium, but there was no vacancy between them. Ramsay's solution was to place argon ahead of potassium, despite its slightly greater atomic weight, because in this way he could put the new element at the bottom of the preceding column, thus adding a new row.

Remember that Mendeléev had composed his table

on the basis of valence. What was argon's valence? Well, the valence of a completely inert element could be considered to be zero. That would fit in nicely with Mendeléev's scheme, for the valence of the elements just before and just after argon was 1. If a zero was inserted between the 1's, creating a new step in each period, all the periods could come out all right, provided a new role was added at the bottom of the table.

Ramsay made bold to add the row: he called it "row O." Argon went in row O at the bottom of the third period, under chlorine. Of course, it opened up a new field of element-hunting. What were the other elements in the new row?

Ramsay started looking for them in the air, reasoning that it probably contained traces of other inert gases besides argon. His hunch was correct. With a co-worker, Morris William Travers, he soon tracked down "neon" (which he named from a Greek word meaning "new"), "krypton" (meaning "hidden"), and "xenon" (meaning "stranger"). All three were inert gases, like argon. Neon fell into place nicely under fluorine at the bottom of the second period, krypton under bromine in the fourth period, and xenon under iodine in the fifth period.

Meanwhile Ramsay had happened on another inert gas in a completely unexpected quarter. An American chemist, William Frances Hillebrand, had detected in a uranium-containing mineral a gas which he thought was nitrogen. Ramsay, being on the lookout for new gases, decided to examine it further. He, too, found the inert gas in a uranium-containing mineral, and he looked at it spectroscopically. Eureka! It showed lines that did not belong to nitrogen. What was more amazing, they were the very same lines that had been discovered in the sun nearly 30 years before and attributed to a solar element called helium by the English astronomer Lockyer (see Chapter 10).

Lockyer had had no idea what sort of element it might be, so he had given its name the common ending "ium," which conventionally meant a metal. Had he guessed it was a gas, he might well have named it "helion."

Helium, the lightest element after hydrogen, naturally fell into place at the bottom of the first period. Ramsay had now filled all the places in the new row from the first to the fifth columns. For his discovery of the "noble" gases he received the Nobel prize in chemistry in 1904.

These elements, with their atomic weights, are listed in Table 19. They brought the total number of known elements to 79.

Table 19

ELEMENT	SYMBOL	ATOMIC WEIGHT	YEAR DISCOVERED	DISCOVERER
Argon	Ar	39.944	1894	{ Rayleigh Ramsay
Helium	He	4.003	1895	Ramsay
Neon	Ne	20.183	1898	{ Ramsay Travers
Krypton	Kr	83.80	1898	{ Ramsay Travers
Xenon	Xe	131.30	1898	{ Ramsey Travers

The periodic table had weathered practically every test. Its general scheme was so sound that the addition of a new row had not disrupted it in any way—in fact, had merely reinforced it. But there was still the sticky problem of that crowded bag of rare-earth elements thrown in with lanthanum. And what about the end of the table—beyond the sixth period? How many elements were still to be found there? How far did the table go?

14

SMALLER THAN THE ATOM

॰

The chemists now had a pretty orderly picture of the elements the universe was made of. But all their discoveries and their organization of the elements had left them farther than ever from an answer to Thales' old question. He had asked, quite reasonably, whether there was some basic substance—some ultimate building block—that made up all the material of the universe. The dozens of different elements the chemists had found only begged that question. What were the *elements* made of?

As early as 1815 an English physician and chemist named William Prout had offered an interesting answer. The hydrogen atom. If you took its atomic weight as 1, then you could suppose that all the other elements were built up from that building block. Carbon, for instance, with an atomic weight of 12, might be considered a tightly bound combination of 12 hydrogen atoms; nitrogen would be composed of 14 hydrogen atoms, sulfur of 32 hydrogen atoms, and so on.

Unfortunately, "Prout's hypothesis" soon tripped over the fact that many elements had an atomic weight which was not a whole-number multiple of hydrogen's. Berzelius' measurements showed that the atomic weight of boron, for instance, was 10.8, chlorine's was 35.5, etc. That would mean boron was made of 10.8 hydrogen atoms! No matter how you sliced it, you couldn't divide the boron atom into hydrogen atoms (or even half-atoms or quarter-atoms). And the situation got worse as the atomic weights of the elements were measured with more and more accuracy. When the measurements were refined to extreme precision at the end of the nineteenth century by the American chemist Theodore William Richards (who got the Nobel prize in chemistry for his work), he found that the atomic weights had to be expressed in fractions running to three decimal places.

This certainly looked like conclusive proof that the hydrogen atom could not be the building block of the elements. And then, in the late 1890's, physicists made a series of dramatic discoveries which killed Prout's premise deader than a doornail (but led to its resurrection in a new form). They found that the hydrogen atom was not the smallest unit of matter after all. In fact, they turned up particles so much tinier that the hydrogen atom itself looked like a huge structure. What's more, the theory that atoms were indivisible broke down completely.

It was a British physicist, Joseph John Thomson, who discovered the first "subatomic" particle. Experimenters with electricity had found that an electric current in a vacuum produced a glowing radiation which they called "cathode rays." Thomson showed that these "rays" consisted of particle's mass was only 1/8000 that of the hydrogen atom. Because it seemed to be the ultimate unit of electricity, it was named the "electron."

Meanwhile the German physicist Wilhelm Konrad

Roentgen, while studying the same cathode rays, had accidentally discovered that they gave rise to a very energetic
penetrating radiation. He called the radiation "X-rays."
Shortly afterward the French physicist Antoine Henry
Becquerel made his famous discovery of radioactivity,
through the accident that a photographic plate he put in
a drawer with some uranium salts was fogged by radiation
from the uranium. This radiation was eventually found to
consist of "alpha rays," "beta rays" (actually electrons),
and "gamma rays."

Uranium was not the only atom that spontaneously
fired out rays and pieces of itself, as physicists soon learned.
There were other radioactive elements. So here, after all
those centuries of belief in the indivisible atom, scientists
had suddenly found atoms breaking up all over the place.

Naturally they set out to see if they could take atoms
apart, or at least explore the atoms' inner structure. The
leader of this exploration was Ernest Rutherford, at the
famous Cavendish Laboratory of the University of Cam-
bridge.

He began to bombard atoms with alpha particles
emitted by radioactive material. Alpha particles are more
than 7,000 times as massive as beta particles, and they
travel at fairly high speed when they are shot out by radioactive atoms. Rutherford set up sheets of thin metal foil in
the path of these tiny bullets. Most of the alpha particles
passed right through the metal foil. But a few were deflected and some bounced back! As Rutherford remarked,
it was as remarkable as if he had fired real bullets at a
sheet of paper and some of them had rebounded.

He decided that the rebounding alpha particles must
have hit very heavy, concentrated targets within the metal
foil. These must be the cores, or nuclei, of metal atoms.
From the fact that most of his bullets passed through the

foil without being deflected, he deduced that the nucleus of each atom must be very small, so small that only one in several thousand of his bullets hit a nucleus. Most of the volume of an atom, therefore, must consist of nearly empty space populated only by the light electrons.

What was the nucleus made of? From the behavior of hydrogen atoms, Rutherford decided that it consisted of one or more positively charged particles which he called "protons." Each nucleus had as many protons as the atom had electrons, so that the proton and electron charges balanced and the atom as a whole was electrically neutral.

The hydrogen atom contained only one proton and one electron. The helium atom had two protons and two electrons; its nucleus, in fact, was the same as an alpha particle.

Rutherford found that he was able to change atoms by chipping out pieces or adding pieces in their nuclei with his alpha-particle bullets. In this way he transformed nitrogen atoms to oxygen atoms in 1919. The old alchemical dream of transmutation was at last achieved, but in a manner that the alchemists had never dreramed of.

RADIOACTIVITY

Thomson, Roentgen, Becquerel, and Rutherford all received Nobel prizes for their work. But the most glamorous of all the Nobel laureates of the turn of the century was Marie Curie, born Marja Sklodowska in Poland in 1867. Marie went to Paris to get an education (at the Sorbonne), and there she met and married a French chemist, Pierre Curie.

Becquerel's discovery of the radiations from uranium fascinated Marie; it was she who suggested the term "radioactivity." With enthusiasm and imagination, she plunged into a career of investigating this phenomenon. Marie began by trying to measure the strength of radioactivity. As the instrument of measurement she used the phenomenon of piezoelectricity, involving the electrical behavior of crystals, which had been discovered by Pierre Curie. Pierre, realizing perhaps that his wife was a greater scientist than he was, abandoned his own research and joined her.

As they measured the radioactivity of samples of uranium ore, they found to their surprise that some samples were many times more radioactive than could be accounted for by the uranium content. This could only mean that other radioactive elements also were present. But if so, the amount must be extremely small, because the Curies were unable to detect any by ordinary chemical analysis. So they decided they would have to collect huge quantities of the ore to get enough of the trace material to analyze. They managed to get tons of ore from mines in Bohemia; the Austrian government had no use for it and was glad to give it away, provided the Curies paid for the transportation. This took almost all their life savings.

They set up shop in a little unheated shed and went to work on their mounds and mounds of uranium ore. Year after year they kept concentrating the radioactivity, discarding inactive material and working with the active. (Marie took time out to have a baby, Irene, who later turned out to be a great scientist on her own.) At last, in July 1898, they succeeded in boiling down their tons of ore to a highly radioactive residue. What they had was a pinch of black powder which was 400 times more radioactive than the same quantity of pure uranium would have been. In this bit of stuff they found a new element resembling tellurium. Mendeléev might have named it "eka-tellurium." The Curies called it "polonium," after Marie's native land.

This element didn't account for all the radioactivity, however. A still more active element must be hiding in their ore. Six months later they finally concentrated that element. Its properties were like those of barium. The element fitted into row IIa in the seventh period of Mendeléev's table. It was the first new element discovered in the seventh period since Berzelius had found thorium 60 years before.

The Curies called the new element "radium," because of its powerful radioactivity.

Pierre Curie died in 1906 as the result of a traffic accident (involving a horse-drawn cab, not one of the new-fangled motor cars). Marie took over his professorship at the Sorbonne and carried on alone. She was the first woman professor in the history of that proud institution. Moreover, she was the only scientist in history to receive two Nobel prizes—one in physics (shared with her husband and Becquerel) for their accurate measurements of radioactivity, and one in chemistry for the discovery of polonium and radium.

Shortly after the Curies tracked down these two rare, radioactive elements, two more were discovered. In 1899 a French chemist, André Louis Debierne, found an element which fitted into row IIIa to the right of lanthanum. He named it "actinium," from a Greek word meaning "ray." Then in 1900 a German physicist, Friedrich Ernst Dorn, detected a highly radioactive gas associated with radium. Ramsay later showed that it was a sixth inert gas belonging with the other noble gases in row O. It was named "radon."

The radioactive elements had taken over the center of the stage. But chemists were still plugging away in the hunt for non-radioactive ones as well. In 1901 a French chemist named Eugène Demarçay, who had helped the Curies to spot radium with the spectroscope, turned up a new rare-earth element which he named "europium," for Europe. Another French chemist, Georges Urbain, also found a rare-earth element to add to the list; he named it "lutetium," after the ancient Roman name for Paris. It was the heaviest rare-earth element identified up to that time.

Table 20 lists the elements discovered in the turn-of-the-century decade.

Table 20

ELEMENTS DISCOVERED IN THE TIME OF THE CURIES

ELEMENT	SYMBOL	ATOMIC WEIGHT	YEAR DISCOVERED	DISCOVERER
Polonium	Po	210	1898	Marie Curie / Pierre Curie
Radium	Ra	226.05	1898	Marie Curie / Pierre Curie
Actinium	Ac	227	1899	Debierne
Radon	Rn	222	1900	Dorn
Europium	Eu	152.0	1901	Demarçay
Lutetium	Lu	174.99	1907	Urbain

ISOTOPES

Most of these elements fitted beautifully into the periodic table. Radon was an inert gas, radium an alkaline-earth element, polonium a relative of tellurium, and actinium a relative of lanthanum. There was a slot for each of them. Furthermore, they helped to fill out the sixth and seventh periods, where there was plenty of room for new elements.

But the radioactive elements introduced new troubles for the table. They grew into a puzzle of no small proportions.

Rutherford and an assistant, Frederick Soddy, realized almost at once that the radioactive elements must be constantly changing. Every time a radioactive atom gave up an alpha particle or a beta particle, it must become a different atom. In other words, spontaneous transmutation was going on all the time.

Each of the radioactive elements had a certain "half-life," as Rutherford called it. This measured the rate of its breakdown—the time it took for half of its atoms to decay into other atoms. Now the half-life of uranium is four and a half billion years; that of thorium, 14 billion years. That's pretty slow: in the whole history of our planet, only a part of these elements has changed. But on the other hand, here are radium, with a half-life of only 1,600 years; actinium, about 22 years; polonium, about four months; and radon, less than four days! There should be practically nothing of these elements left on our old planet. In fact, there wouldn't be if it were not that small amounts of them are constantly being formed by the breakdown of heavier elements.

The periodic-table puzzle arose when chemists began to look into the products of the decay of radioactive elements. They found three different series of products, named the "uranium series," the "thorium series," and the "actinium series," after the starting element in each case. Very quickly the chemists identified more than 40 new "elements" among these products!

All three series ended with lead: that was the final, stable element into which they decayed. (What a crowning irony for the alchemists: transmutations ended in lead, instead of the other way around!) If lead was the end product, then all the transitional elements formed by the radioactive decay of the heavier elements must lie between lead and uranium in atomic weight. The trouble was, there were only three vacancies left in the periodic table in that interval. How could you fit more than 40 elements into three vacancies?

Rutherford's colleague, Soddy, eventually (in 1913) came up with the answer. They weren't 40 different elements; they were merely varieties of just a few elements. A single element might have a number of different forms, differing slightly in atomic weight and with different radioactivities. Chemically, all would belong in the same place in the periodic table. Soddy called them "isotopes," from Greek words meaning the "same place."

Just how an element could exist in different atomic weights did not become clear until 1932, when a new subatomic particle was discovered by the English physicist James Chadwick. The particle is the neutron, which has about the same mass as the proton but no electric charge. It brought to light the fact that the nucleus of an atom in almost every case contains neutrons as well as protons.

Now, to take the simplest case, consider a nucleus made up of one proton and one neutron. Since there is only one positive charge in the nucleus, the atom will have only one electron outside the nucleus. As far as the atom's chemical behavior is concerned, the electron is the important thing; the nucleus has nothing to do, directly, with the atom's chemical properties. The chemical activity of every element is determined by the number and arrangement of its electrons; this dictates what kinds of compounds it can form.

Thus hydrogen is hydrogen because it has one electron, and so on for the other elements. The hydrogen atom always has just one proton, allowing it one electron. But its nucleus may also contain one or two neutrons. The ordinary variety of hydrogen has no neutron in its nucleus. Every sample of hydrogen in nature, however, also includes small amounts of the two rarer "isotopes," containing one or two neutrons, respectively.

This explained why elements had varieties with different atomic weights. The hydrogen isotope with a neutron and a proton in its nucleus has an atomic weight of 2, of course, since the neutron's weight is about equal to a proton's. Likewise, the hydrogen isotope containing two neutrons and a proton has an atomic weight of 3. The same goes for the varieties of all the other elements: the atomic weights of their isotopes vary according to the number of neutrons in their nuclei. The presence of extra neutrons, or of fewer than the usual number, doesn't affect the chemical properties of the element, since they depend on the number of electrons, which in turn is determined only by the number of protons.

In the case of uranium, the nucleus of the common form of the atom has 92 protons and 146 neutrons, giving it a total of 238 "nucleons" (nuclear particles) and therefore an atomic weight of 238. This is known as uranium-238, or U^{238}. Its famous fissionable brother, uranium-235, has three fewer neutrons. This nucleus is less stable, or more radioactive, so its half-life is only 700 million years, as against uranium-238's four and half billion years.

The isotope theory at once accounted for the 40-odd species of elements discovered between uranium and lead. They were, in fact, isotopes of just a few elements. But the theory did much more than that. It showed for the first time why the atomic weights of most of the elements were not whole numbers. The reason was simply that the elements as found in nature were mixtures of isotopes.

The radioactive elements are not the only ones composed of isotopes. Many stable elements also turned out to be made up of two or more different species of atoms. This was shown by an instrument called the "mass spectrograph," developed by the English physicist Francis William Aston, an assistant of Thomson. It separates stable atoms of different weights by firing them into a magnetic field, where they take different paths according to their weights. With this instrument Aston found that, in the element neon, nine-tenths of the atoms had an atomic weight of 20 and one-tenth had a weight of 22. This explained why the average weight of neon was 20.2. (Another isotope, neon-21, was discovered later, but it is so rare that it doesn't affect the weight of the element appreciably.)

Chlorine's atomic weight of 35.5 was clarified in the same way. Three-fourths of its atoms have a weight of 35 and one-fourth weigh 37 (two extra neutrons). Thus we say that chlorine is made up of two isotopes of "mass numbers" 35 and 37.

In some cases the uncommon isotopes are so rare that the atomic weight of the element is virtually a whole number. In nitrogen, for instance, only four atoms out of 1,000 have a mass number of 15: all the rest are nitrogen-14. So the atomic weight of nitrogen is just about 14.

A few elements have atoms of only one weight. The only variety of fluorine found in nature, for example, is fluorine-19. Naturally the element's atomic weight is exactly 19.

Prout turned out to be not so wrong after all. If he had said that all the elements were built up from the nucleus of hydrogen (the proton), he would have been close to the mark. What he didn't reckon with, and couldn't, was the neutron—a hard-to-detect particle weighing the same as the proton.

15

RANK-ORDER OF THE ELEMENTS

↺

The discoveries I discussed in the last chapter, to use a popular word of the moment, "down-graded" the importance of atomic weight. This property was not, after all, the decisive one in identifying the elements. Here, for instance, were three forms of lead with different atomic weights— lead-206, lead-207, and lead-208 (the end products of radioactive decay of the uranium, actinium, and thorium series respectively). In spite of their different weights, all three were lead; chemically speaking, they were identical triplets. What, then, distinguished one element from another? What made lead lead?

I have already touched on the answer in the last chapter: the decisive feature of an element is the number of protons in its nucleus. But in science nothing is ever self-evident. Discoveries and knowledge are won only by hard, probing labor. In the early 1900's, atomic scientists had only the dimmest notions of what lay inside the atom, and the existence of neutrons was not even suspected.

The answer to the question about the elements was

discovered in what we might consider a roundabout way and with what may seem an unlikely tool—X-rays.

A British physicist named Charles Glover Barkla had found that each element, on being struck by X-rays, scattered them in a particular way; that is, each produced its own "characteristic X-rays." This led another young British physicist, Henry Gwyn-Jeffreys Moseley, to make a systematic study of the elements with X-rays as a probe.

As he went down the list of elements, Moseley found that the wavelength of the characteristic X-rays became progressively shorter as the atomic weight increased. He decided that the wavelength reflected the size of the electrons' orbit around the nucleus of the atom. Probably the electrons were responsible for the emissions of X-rays. The closer the electrons were to the nucleus, the smaller would be their orbit, and the tighter the orbit, the shorter the wavelength of the X-rays emitted. So he reasoned.

Now, the wavelength decreased with the weight of the atom. In the heavier atoms, then, the electrons must be drawn closer to the nucleus. What was the force that drew them closer? It must be an increase in the nucleus' positive charge, attracting the negatively charged electrons. In other words, the nuclear charge must increase from element to element right through the periodic table. The most reasonable way to account for this is to suppose that each element has one more unit of positive charge (*i.e.,* one more proton) than the one before.

The table starts with hydrogen—one positive charge. After it, on the basis of charge, come helium (two charges), lithium (three charges), and so on. Thus the elements can be listed by "atomic number," referring to the number of positive charges in the nucleus.

Once Moseley's discovery was published, chemists began to assign atomic numbers to element after element.

Table 21 lists all the elements then known in order of increasing atomic number. The heaviest known element, uranium, was Number 92.

The atomic number at once proved to be much more useful than the atomic weight for organizing the table of elements. For instance, in terms of atomic weight there was a substantial gap between hydrogen (1.0080) and helium (4.003). It left room for an element with an atomic weight of around 3, say. But their respective atomic numbers of 1 and 2, meaning that the hydrogen atom contained one proton and the helium atom only two, definitely ruled out the possibility of any element occurring between them. On the other hand, a missing atomic number in the list definitely meant a missing element. In short, the use of atomic numbers pinpointed all the missing elements and also made it plain when elements were *not* missing.

Furthermore, the atomic-number system solved the mystery of the few elements that had to be placed in the wrong order of atomic weight in the periodic table. Take the case of tellurium and iodine. On chemical grounds, Mendeléev had had to put tellurium ahead of iodine, although its atomic weight was greater. Now it developed that, according to the nuclear charge, Mendeléev had been right: tellurium has 52 protons and iodine 53. The reason tellurium has a higher atomic weight is that its isotopes load the element on the heavy side. It has seven isotopes, and the most common is the heaviest one—tellurium-128. Iodine, on the other hand, comes in only one form—iodine-127. So tellurium as found in nature is slightly heavier.

The same sort of thing accounts for the argon-potassium and cobalt-nickel switches in the periodic table; argon is slightly heavier than potassium, and cobalt than nickel, because of an imbalance in the atomic weights of their isotopes.

Table 21

ELEMENTS IN THE ORDER OF ATOMIC NUMBER

1 — Hydrogen	30 — Zinc
2 — Helium	31 — Gallium
3 — Lithium	32 — Germanium
4 — Beryllium	33 — Arsenic
5 — Boron	34 — Selenium
6 — Carbon	35 — Bromine
7 — Nitrogen	36 — Krypton
8 — Oxygen	37 — Rubidium
9 — Fluorine	38 — Strontium
10 — Neon	39 — Yttrium
11 — Sodium	40 — Zirconium
12 — Magnesium	41 — Niobium
13 — Aluminum	42 — Molybdenum
14 — Silicon	43 — ————
15 — Phosphorus	44 — Ruthenium
16 — Sulfur	45 — Rhodium
17 — Chlorine	46 — Palladium
18 — Argon	47 — Silver
19 — Potassium	48 — Cadmium
20 — Calcium	49 — Indium
21 — Scandium	50 — Tin
22 — Titanium	51 — Antimony
23 — Vanadium	52 — Tellurium
24 — Chromium	53 — Iodine
25 — Manganese	54 — Xenon
26 — Iron	55 — Cesium
27 — Cobalt	56 — Barium
28 — Nickel	57 — Lanthanum
29 — Copper	58 — Cerium

59 — Praseodymium	76 — Osmium
60 — Neodymium	77 — Iridium
61 — ———	78 — Platinum
62 — Samarium	79 — Gold
63 — Europium	80 — Mercury
64 — Gadolinium	81 — Thallium
65 — Terbium	82 — Lead
66 — Dysprosium	83 — Bismuth
67 — Holmium	84 — Polonium*
68 — Erbium	85 — ———
69 — Thulium	86 — Radon*
70 — Ytterbium	87 — ———
71 — Lutetium	88 — Radium*
72 — ———	89 — Actinium*
73 — Tantalum	90 — Thorium*
74 — Tungsten	91 — ———
75 — ———	92 — Uranium*

Moseley did not live to see how beautifully his discovery of the atomic numbers worked out. In 1915, at the age of 27, he was killed by a bullet in the battle of Gallipoli. It was a tragic loss of one of the best minds in science.

THE NINETY-TWO ELEMENTS

Table 21 shows that all the known elements in Moseley's time beyond the atomic number 83 were radioactive. Of these heavy elements, only thorium and uranium are long-lived. Chemists felt certain that the missing elements 85, 87, and 91 would prove to be radioactive and short-lived. In all likelihood they were transitory products of the decay of uranium and thorium.

* Radioactive

In 1917 element 91 was tracked down, and sure enough, it confirmed the prediction. Its discoverers were Otto Hahn and Lise Meitner (who were later to become much more famous for their discovery of uranium fission). Working in Berlin, these two scientists broke down pitch-blende with hot acid to separate its elements. After they had removed all traces of radium and other known radioactive elements, they found a radioactive remnant which proved to be element 91. This decayed into actinium, so it was named "protactinium." Soddy and some of his co-workers discovered protactinium independently, but Hahn and Meitner published first.

Atomic scientists felt sure that any elements beyond 92 (uranium) would be so short-lived that no surviving trace of them would be found in nature. Uranium, then, for all practical purposes, was the end of the periodic table. The universe was made up of just 92 elements.

There were still a few gaps—a few prizes still to be unearthed by the element-hunters. Among these there appeared to be two missing rare-earth elements: atomic numbers 61 and 72.

Urbain, the discoverer of lutetium in the early 1800's, had thought he had detected number 72 in rare-earth material. He called his find "celtium," after the Celts of ancient France. But X-ray analysis showed that "celtium" was actually a mixture of lutetium and ytterbium. Urbain's "discovery" was one of a long list of false alarms which this book is not long enough to tell about.

The Danish physicist Niels Bohr finally decided, from his studies of the electron arrangement in atoms, that element 72 was not a rare-earth element at all. Number 72 belonged in row IVa next to zirconium and must resemble that metal. And so it turned out. In 1923 the German physicist Dirk Coster and the Hungarian chemist Georg von

Hevesy, working in Copenhagen, examined some apparently purified zirconium compounds with X-rays. The X-rays revealed that another element, very much like zirconium, was mixed with it. They named it "hafnium," after the Latin name of Copenhagen. Hafnium is not a very rare element; the reason it had not been identified earlier is that it is almost a chemical twin of zirconium.

Three German chemists, Walter Noddack, Ida Tacke, and Otto Berg, made a systematic X-ray search of certain minerals for new elements, and in 1925 they were rewarded by the discovery of element number 75. They named it "rhenium," for the Rhine River. It was not radioactive, and in fact was the last of the stable elements to be discovered.

Table 22 lists the new elements discovered in the decade after Moseley.

Table 22

ELEMENTS DISCOVERED IN THE DECADE AFTER MOSELEY

ELEMENT	SYMBOL	ATOMIC NUMBER	ATOMIC WEIGHT	YEAR DISCOVERED	DISCOVERER
Protactinium	Pa	91	231	1917	{ Hahn { Meitner
Hafnium	Hf	72	178.50	1923	{ Coster { Hevesy
Rhenium	Re	75	186.22	1925	{ Noddack { Tacke { Berg

By 1925, then, the search for the elements had uncovered 88, of which 81 were stable and seven redioactive. Only four were still missing: numbers 43, 61, 85, and 87.

In the following decade several hunters thought they found one or another of these elements. But these claims turned out to be mistaken. The last four holdouts eluded discovery until the arrival of what we call "the atomic age."

ELECTRON SHELLS

Meanwhile Niels Bohr of Copenhagen solved the se-cret of the periodic table. Mendeléev, of course, had had no idea why the elements fell into periods, rows, and cozy family groups. Generations of chemists tried to find the ex-planation. Bohr discovered the answer in the arrangement of the atoms' electrons.

He got his information from the spectral pictures of the elements. Their patterns of spectral lines suggested to him that the electrons circling around the nucleus of an atom were confined to certain definite orbits or "shells." There was room for only a certain number of electrons in each shell. The first shell could hold two electrons. Thus hydrogen, with one electron, and helium, with two, had a single electron-shell. After this shell was filled, the addi-tion of further electrons formed a second shell containing up to six electrons. These accounted for the next six elements. Then came a third shell with room for eight electrons. And so on.

How exactly this fitted the periodic table! Each shell represented a period. As for the rows, each was distin-guished by the fact that all the elements in it had the same number of electrons in the last, or outer, shell.

The number of electrons in that outermost shell is the most important factor determining an element's chemical behavior. It fixes the element's valence and dictates how the element can combine with other elements.

Let us look at row Ia. Hydrogen has one electron. The next element in the row, lithium (atomic number 3), has three electrons—two in the first shell and one in the second. The next, sodium (atomic number 11), has eleven electrons

—two in the first shell, eight in the second, and one in the third. The same thing holds for the other elements in row Ia: potassium has one electron in its outer shell (the fourth), so have rubidium (in the fifth shell) and cesium (in the sixth shell). The chemical kinship of these elements is manifested in the fact that, except for hydrogen (an element which in many ways is unique), all of them form a family—the alkali metals.

Likewise, all the alkaline-earth elements—beryllium, magnesium, calcium, strontium, barium, and radium—have in common the presence of *two* electrons in their outermost shell. Seven electrons in the outer shell mark the halogens—fluorine, chlorine, bromine, and iodine (all in row VIIb). A filled outer shell, containing eight electrons, marks the inert gases—neon, argon, krypton, xenon, and radon. And so it goes for the other rows.

Bohr's electron-shell model was later modified: it turned out that each shell was divided into subshells. That helped to explain some oddities: cases of chemical kinship which seemed to contradict the electron-shell theory. For instance, iron, cobalt, and nickel all have the same valence and are chemically alike despite the fact that they contain 26, 27, and 28 electrons, respectively. How can they have the same number of electrons in the outer shell when each has just one more electron than the one before? The answer is that the successive electrons are added not to the outermost shell but to the subshell below it. Thus the outer shells *are* the same in these three cases.

This is a general feature of the heavier elements in the periodic table. As the atomic number goes up, the electrons are not added in a strictly regular order, filling each shell before they start the next. Some may go into a new outer shell while the one below still has holes in it. As a matter of fact, holes may be left in a shell *two* levels below the outer one. Then, at a certain point, additional electrons start filling the holes in the inner shells instead of going into the outer shell.

That is what happens in the series of rare-earth elements. In these 14 elements, each successive electron is added to the shell buried two levels below. Therefore all 14 have the same number of electrons in their outermost shell. The added electron that distinguishes each element from the next is buried so deeply that it has little effect on chemical behavior. That is why the 14 rare-earth elements, starting with lanthanum, are so much alike.

16

THE MAN-MADE
ELEMENTS

Man at last understood the elements well enough to make his own. In the twentieth century he became an alchemist who knew what he was doing—up to a point.

First there were those four elements still missing from the periodic table. The fact was, they were practically missing from nature, too. Scientists had to make these elements themselves to study them.

As I have mentioned, in 1919 Ernest Rutherford changed nitrogen to oxygen by bombarding nitrogen atoms with alpha particles. This suggested that all one had to do to alter an element artificially was to add or subtract particles in its nucleus.

The first completely new, man-made isotope, indeed, was created by Rutherford's method. Its creators were Irene Curie, the daughter of the famous Marie and Pierre, and her husband Frederic Joliot. (To perpetuate the Curie name, Joliot changed his name to Joliot-Curie when he married Irene.)

The Joliot-Curies bombarded aluminum with alpha particles. Their attack transformed some of the aluminum atoms into a highly radioactive substance. This proved to be a new kind of phosphorus. Its atomic weight was 30, instead of natural phosphorus' 31. (As the discovery of the neutron was to show later, the nucleus of phosphorus-30 has 15 neutrons instead of the 16 in nature's phosphorus.)

It was no wonder that phosphorus-30 did not occur in nature; its half-life was only two and a half minutes. At all events, the Joliot-Curies had produced "artificial radioactivity" for the first time. Irene, like her mother before her, received the Nobel prize in physics in 1935 along with her husband.

FILLING THE LAST HOLES

The era of artificial transmutation really began with the building of the first "atom-smasher"—the cyclotron—by Ernest Orlando Lawrence at the University of California in 1931. With the cyclotron, and the vastly more energetic particle-accelerators developed later, it became possible to open up the nucleus of any atom, to add particles to it, and even to create altogether new particles.

The first element produced in this way was the missing number 43. A claim to discovery of this element had been made in 1925 by Noddack, Tacke, and Berg, the discoverers of rhenium. They had named element number 43 "masurium" (after a district in East Prussia). But no one else was able to find "masurium" in the same source material, so their supposed discovery had remained a question mark. It was, in fact, just a mistake. In 1937 Emilio Gino Segrè of Italy, an ardent hunter for the element, identified the real number 43.

Lawrence had bombarded a sample of molybdenum (element number 42) with protons accelerated in his cyclotron. Finally he got some radioactive stuff which he sent to Segrè in Italy for analysis. Segrè and an assistant,

C. Perrier, traced some of the radioactivity to an element which behaved like manganese. Since the missing element 43 belonged in a vacancy in the periodic table next to manganese, they were sure this was it.

It turned out that element number 43 had several isotopes. Oddly, all of them were radioactive. There were no stable isotopes of the element!

This was surprising. Every other element up to bismuth (number 83) had at least one stable isotope. No one could understand why an element with an atomic number as low as 43 should have only radioactive forms.

Nevertheless, facts are facts. Element number 43 indeed is totally unstable. Its longest-lived isotope, with a mass number of 99, has a half-life of only a little more than 200,000 years. Therefore all of the element that may originally have been formed in nature must have broken down early in the history of our billions-of-years-old planet.

Segrè named element number 43 "technetium," from a Greek word meaning "artificial," because it was the first element made by man.

The next of the missing elements to be discovered was number 87. This one was actually detected in nature. In 1939 Marguerite Perey, a French chemist, found a new type of radiation among the products of the radioactive decay of actinium. The radiation proved to belong to an element which behaved like an alkali-metal. Therefore it had to be element number 87, the missing member of the alkali-metal family. The Frenchwoman named it "francium."

The amount of francium she found was only a bare trace. The element was later produced artificially by an accelerator, however, and only then did chemists obtain enough of it for detailed study. For that reason francium is usually considered one of the man-made elements.

It was Segrè, again, who turned up the next of the

missing elements. He left Fascist Italy in 1938 and went to work in the Radiation Laboratory at the University of California. With two colleagues there, D. R. Corson and K. R. Mackenzie, he bombarded bismuth with alpha particles. This maneuver succeeded in adding the alpha particle's two protons to the bismuth nucleus, forming element number 85. Because the new element had no stable isotopes, it was named "astatine," from a Greek word meaning "unstable." Later, traces of astatine were found in nature as a breakdown product of uranium.

By 1940, then, three of the last four holes had been filled. The element still missing from the table of 92 elements was number 61. This one emerged in an entirely new way. It was not produced deliberately but turned up as a dividend of the discovery of nuclear fission.

After Chadwick found the neutron in 1932, physicists realized at once that it was a wonderful tool for investigating atomic nuclei and perhaps forming new elements. As an uncharged particle, it would not be repelled by the positively-charged nucleus.

One of the first to start bombarding nuclei with neutrons was the great Italian physicist Enrico Fermi. In the middle 1930's Fermi and his associates in Rome performed many experiments with neutrons. Among other things, they bombarded uranium with the particle, hoping to create elements beyond uranium. They thought they actually succeeded in doing this, but they could not prove it. In fact, they got some products that baffled them and other physicists for several years.

The upshot of this mystery is now a familar story: how Otto Hahn in Germany discovered that one of these products was barium, an element only about half the weight of uranium; how his old partner Lise Meitner, who had fled from the Nazis to Sweden, became convinced that neutron bombardment had split the uranium atom in two ("uranium fission") and boldly published this revolutionary conclusion; how Fermi and other physicists, many of them refugees to the United States from the European dictatorships, eventually produced a fission chain reaction and the atomic bomb.

The point that concerns us here is that the fission of uranium produced dozens of different "fission products," many of them new isotopes not previously known. And in 1948 three chemists at the Oak Ridge National Laboratory —J. A. Marinsky, L. E. Glendenin, and C. D. Coryell— found element number 61 among the fission products. As chemists had suspected, all the isotopes of the element proved to be radioactive: the longest-lived has a half-life of only about 30 years. No wonder it couldn't be found in nature!

The discoverers named the element "promethium," after Prometheus, because it had been created in the hot fire of a nuclear furnace.

And so the last hole in the periodic table was filled. But promethium was not to be the end of the search for the elements.

BEYOND 92

Ninety-two was not the limit after all. Fermi, who thought he had made element number 93 and called it "uranium X," turned out to be not altogether wrong. His melange of products from the bombardment of uranium did include element 93, though he could not identify it.

In 1940 Edwin M. McMillan at the University of California discovered traces of an element in neutron-bombarded uranium which he thought might be number

93. What kind of element would it be? In the seventh period of the periodic table, actinium (element 89) was known to be chemically similar to lanthanum. Did that mean it started a second series of rare-earth elements, like the one following lanthanum? If so, actinium, thorium, protactinium, uranium, and element 93 would all be rare-earth metals.

The chemistry of these elements was not very well known at the time. About the only thing chemists had to go on was that some of the properties of uranium seemed to resemble those of tungsten. This would mean that uranium was *not* a rare-earth. And if uranium belonged next to tungsten in the table, then element 93 should be like rhenium, the element after tungsten in the sixth period.

McMillan asked Segrè to analyze his sample of "element 93." Segrè found that it did not resemble rhenium; it was actually more like a rare-earth.

McMillan and his assistant, Philip Abelson, soon established that their substance was definitely element number 93. McMillan named it "neptunium," for Neptune, the planet beyond Uranus, from which uranium had got its name.

McMillan then left for war work and turned his research over to Glenn Theodore Seaborg at California. Seaborg promptly discovered that radioactive neptunium gave rise to another new element—number 94. When neptunium decayed, it emitted an electron from its nucleus, and one of its neutrons changed to a proton. That raised the number of protons from 93 to 94, so it became a new element. The element was named "plutonium," after Pluto, the planet beyond Neptune.

Both neptunium and plutonium behaved like the rare-earths chemically, confirming that the elements beginning with actinium did indeed form a second rare-earth series. To distinguish the two series, the first group (beginning with lanthanum) became known as the "lanthanides" and the second as the "actinides."

The longest-lived isotope of neptunium, with a mass number of 237, has a half-life of a little over two million years. Of the plutonium and neptunium originally present in the earth, no detectable trace is left. But tiny amounts of them must be formed continually by cosmic-ray neutrons striking uranium in the soil and rocks. Traces of these elements have indeed been detected in uranium ore.

If neptunium and plutonium could be made artificially, why not go on to produce more transuranium elements? Under the leadership of Seaborg, the California group set out on a systematic program to see how far they could go. They bombarded each transuranium element successively to form ones with higher atomic numbers. The job was not easy, and it got harder from element to element. The half-lives of the successive elements were shorter and shorter, so it was more and more difficult to collect enough of each element to make the next one.

In 1944 Seaborg and two assistants, R. A. James and L. O. Morgan, succeeded in achieving element 95 by bombarding uranium with alpha particles. Since 95 matched europium in the first rare-earth series, it was named "americium," after America.

Later that year Seaborg, James, and A. Ghiorso tracked down element 96, this time made by bombarding plutonium with alpha particles. As a counterpart of the rare-earth gadolinium (named for the element-hunter Gadolin), number 96 was named "curium," after the Curies.

In 1949 Seaborg, Ghiorso, and S. G. Thompson announced that by bombarding americium with alpha particles they had formed element 97. The following year these three workers and K. Street made number 98 by bombarding curium with alpha particles. In honor of the place where the elements were being discovered, numbers 97 and 98 respectively were named "berkelium" (after Berkeley, the university town) and "californium."

Table 23

THE MAN-MADE ELEMENTS

Element	Symbol	Atomic Number	Year Discovered	Discoverer
Technetium	Tc	43	1937	Segrè / Perrier
Francium	Fr	87	1939	Perey
Astatine	At	85	1940	Corson / Mackenzie / Segrè
Neptunium	Np	93	1940	McMillan / Abelson
Plutonium	Pu	94	1940	McMillan / Seaborg
Americium	Am	95	1944	American team
Curium	Cm	96	1944	American team
Promethium	Pm	61	1948	American team
Berkelium	Bk	97	1949	American team
Californium	Cf	98	1950	American team
Einsteinium	Es	99	1955	American team
Fermium	Fm	100	1955	American team
Mendelevium	Md	101	1955	American team
Nobelium	No	102	1957	International team
Lawrencium	Lw	103	1961	American team

The next elements came out of the terrifying explosion of the first hydrogen bomb in 1952. In the debris from that explosion scientists detected traces of what seemed to be 99 and 100. These elements were later made in the laboratory and announced in 1955. In naming them, the discoverers chose to commemorate Albert Einstein and Enrico Fermi; element 99 was called "einsteinium" and number 100 was named "fermium."

In 1955 a team of chemists including Seaborg and Chiorso bombarded einsteinium with alpha particles and produced a few atoms of element number 101. This was named, at long last, in honor of Mendeléev: "mendelevium."

In 1957 teams of chemists in the United States, Great Britain, and Sweden reported the isolation of element number 102. Because part of the work was done at the Nobel Institute in Stockholm, it was named "nobelium."

In 1961 an American team produced element 103 and suggested that it be named "lawrencium" for Lawrence, the inventor of the cyclotron.

Lawrencium rounded out the rare-earth series. The scientists went on to look for element 104, hopefully expecting that it would resemble hafnium, the first element after the lanthanides.

In Table 23 I list the man-made elements. All, of course, are radioactive. We can't assign true atomic weights to them, because they don't occur in nature and not all of their possible isotopes are known.

As of the time of writing, then, the list of known elements totals 103. Their arrangement in the periodic table is shown in Table 24. (Usually the periodic table is written with the periods running horizontally and the rows vertically, but I have done it the other way in order to have room for the full names of the elements, instead of just their symbols.)

EPILOGUE

The search for the elements is just about completed, except possibly for a few fleeting traces of substances beyond

Table 24

THE Periodic Table AS IT LOOKS NOW

	First Period	Second Period	Third Perio
row Ia	1 – Hydrogen	3 – Lithium	11 – Sodium
row IIa		4 – Beryllium	12 – Magnesiur
row IIIa			
row IVa			
row Va			
row VIa			
row VIIa			
row VIII			
row Ib			
row IIb			
row IIIb		5 – Boron	13 – Aluminum
row IVb		6 – Carbon	14 – Silicon
row Vb		7 – Nitrogen	15 – Phosphoru
row VIb		8 – Oxygen	16 – Sulfur
row VIIb		9 – Fluorine	17 – Chlorine
row O	2 – Helium	10 – Neon	18 – Argon

Table 24 (cont.)

Fourth Period	Fifth Period	Sixth Period	Seventh Period
9–Potassium	37–Rubidium	55–Cesium	87–Francium *
0–Calcium	38–Strontium	56–Barium	88–Radium *
1–Scandium	39–Yttrium	57–Lanthanum	89–Actinium *
		58–Cerium	90–Thorium *
		59–Praseodymium	91–Protactinium *
		60–Neodymium	92–Uranium *
		61–Promethium *	93–Neptunium *
		62–Samarium	94–Plutonium *
		63–Europium	95–Americium *
		64–Gadolinium	96–Curium *
		65–Terbium	97–Berkelium *
		66–Dysprosium	98–Californium *
		67–Holmium	99–Einsteinium *
		68–Erbium	100–Fermium *
		69–Thulium	101–Mendelevium *
		70–Ytterbium	102–Nobelium *
		71–Lutetium	103–Lawrencium *
2–Titanium	40–Zirconium	72–Hafnium	
3–Vanadium	41–Niobium	73–Tantalum	
4–Chromium	42–Molybdenum	74–Tungsten	
5–Manganese	43–Technetium *	75–Rhenium	
6–Iron	44–Ruthenium	76–Osmium	
7–Cobalt	45–Rhodium	77–Iridium	
8–Nickel	46–Palladium	78–Platinum	
9–Copper	47–Silver	79–Gold	
0–Zinc	48–Cadmium	80–Mercury	
1–Gallium	49–Indium	81–Thallium	
2–Germanium	50–Tin	82–Lead	
3–Arsenic	51–Antimony	83–Bismuth	
4–Selenium	52–Tellurium	84–Polonium *	
5–Bromine	53–Iodine	85–Astatine *	
6–Krypton	54–Xenon	86–Radon *	

* Radioactive

lawrencium which man may yet contrive to manufacture. But Thales is still waiting for the answer to his question: What is the universe made of?

The elements, it would seem, are made of protons, neutrons, and electrons. A generation ago that was offered as the ultimate answer to Thales. But in the last 30 years this neat, clean-cut solution has gone up in thin smoke. The physicists, investigating protons, neutrons, and electrons in ways involving some pretty rough handling, have released an astonishing and bewildering multitude of other particles. Some 30 different subatomic particles have now been discovered, and labeled with question-begging names such as meson, neutrino, K, lambda, sigma, and xi. So the scientists are wrestling heroically with the same old question in a new form:

What are the subatomic particles made of?

The mysteries of the universe and the questions that scientists strive to answer never come to an end. For that we should be grateful. A universe in which there were no mysteries for curious men to ponder would be a very dull universe indeed.

INDEX

153

Brandt, George, 35
Brass, 20
Bromine, 67, 82
Bunsen, Robert Wilhelm, 83

Cadmium, 69
Cagliostro, Allesandro di, 32
Calcium, 66, 81
Calcium sulfate, 81
Californium, 148
Callinicus, 11
Caloric, 52
Calx, 33, 47
Cannizzaro, Stanislao, 77
Carbon, 29
Carbon dioxide, 26, 40, 56
Carbon monoxide, 18, 56
Carlisle, Anthony, 63
Catalysis, 82
Cathode rays, 121
Cavendish, Henry, 38, 49, 115
Celsus, Aulus Cornelius, 20
Celtium, 136
Cerium, 59
Cesium, 84
Chadwick, James, 128
Charles I, 27
Charles II, 27, 31
Charles III, 37
Chemistry, 27
  nomenclature of, 51
Chlorine, 43, 82, 130
Christian IV, 32
Chromium, 59
Cleve, Per Theodor, 110, 113
Cobalt, 35
Columbium, 60
Combustion, 47
Constantinople, 11
Copernicus, Nicolas, 23
Copper, 21, 29, 35
Copper arsenite, 42
Copper carbonate, 55
Corson, D. R., 144
Coryell, C. D., 145
Coster, Dirk, 136
Courtois, Bernard, 67
Cronstedt, Axel Fredrik, 35
Crookes, William, 84

Cuprum, 74
Curie, Irene, 124, 141
Curie, Marie, 123
Curie, Pierre, 123
Curium, 147
Cyclotron, 142

Dalton, John, 55ff., 72
Davy, Humphry, 63
Debierne, Andre Louis, 125
Definite proportions, law of, 55
Demarçay, Eugène, 125
Democritus, 54
Dephlogisticated air, 41
Diamond, 112
Didymium, 78
Diocletian, 11
Döbereiner, Johann Wolfgang, 81
Döbereiner's lamp, 82
Dorn, Friedrich Ernst, 125
Dysprosium, 113

Earth ("element"), 5, 28, 46, 54
Earth (oxide), 59
Edward I, 19
Egypt, 9
Einstein, Albert, 149
Einsteinium, 149
Eka-aluminum, 106, 109
Eka-boron, 107, 110
Eka-silicon, 106, 110
Ekeberg, Anders Gustaf, 60
Electricity, 62ff.
Electron, 121
Electron shells, 138
Element, 3
  atomic number of, 132, 134-135
  atomic volume of, 94
  atomic weight of, 56, 75, 80ff., 88ff., 120, 121, 128ff.
  composition of, 120ff.
  definition of, 27
  differences among, 53ff.
  four, 5, 6
  heavenly bodies and, 86
  Lavoisier's list of, 52, 62
  missing, 106
  periodic table of, 102, 103, 150-151